CW00400746

Sir William ~~Stanier~~

A New Biography

by
John Chacksfield
FBIS, MRAeS, AFAIAA, C. Eng

THE OAKWOOD PRESS

© Oakwood Press & John Chacksfield 2001

British Library Cataloguing in Publication Data
A Record for this book is available from the British Library
ISBN 0 85361 576 4

Typeset by Oakwood Graphics.
Repro by Ford Graphics, Ringwood, Hants.
Printed by Inkon Printers Ltd, Yateley, Hants.

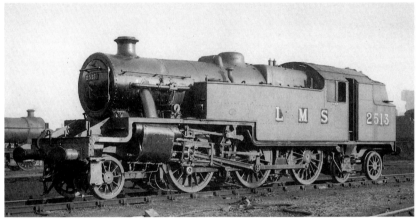

This 3-cylinder 2-6-4T sports a replacement domed boiler. Found at Derby on 25th November, 1947.   *J.M. Jarvis*

Title page: Stanier 2-6-2T No. 126 takes shape at Derby works on 1st September, 1936.
R.S. Carpenter Collection

Front cover (top): Portrait photograph.   *W.M. Stanier*
Front cover (bottom): A postcard view of the 'Coronation Scot'.   *J. Alsop Collection*
Rear cover (top): Colour postcard of Stanier Pacific No. 6255 *City of Hereford.*
J. Alsop Collection
Rear cover (bottom): A postcard from the same series of '8F' class 2-8-0 No. 8111.
J. Alsop Collection

Published by The Oakwood Press (Usk), P.O. Box 13, Usk, Mon., NP15 1YS.
E-mail: oakwood-press@dial.pipex.com
Website: www.oakwood-press.dial.pipex.com

Contents

A photograph of William Stanier at his desk in the late 1930s.

W.M. *Stanier*

Foreword

This book is a magnificent record of facts hitherto largely unrecorded yet highly relevant to the success of those machines whose engineering design was directly influenced by William Stanier. The essence of this success, so faithfully recorded in this book, is the principle of 'keep it as simple as possible'. This was the hallmark of the Swindon products from which these subsequent designs were derived, and it was of great benefit to the LMS.

Also well portrayed in the book are many family details and references to the world outside work, which have not generally come to light previously. Indeed, avoidance of much of the technical material already published makes the book much more informative.

It is very refreshing and unusual to find such detail not only on the subject, but also his predecessors who had such an effect on his development and the way he approached the requirements presented to him. Also notable are the various minor incidents and observations which give much background to the scenes covered.

William Stanier would freely admit today, looking back on his career, that as well as his obvious ability, he was in the right place at the right time. The daunting task confronting him on appointment as CME of the LMS could be tackled on the basis of what he had seen and experienced at Swindon, where the Great Western was already well down the path of equipping itself with a collection of highly successful standard designs. The die was already cast, so the right team had to be assembled, and the description of this in the book is illuminating.

He also had the essential experience of drawing office, test running and maintenance denied to Henry Fowler, which were invaluable in effectively tackling the job which confronted him. He set to work with great ability, but not without what today would be called 'teething problems'. Here also the influence of previous experience is quite clear, in that whilst not everything can be transferred successfully to a different situation, the solutions developed were based on simplicity and common sense.

His visits overseas are covered, with details of the work involved, from 'King' class locomotive and train on exhibition in the USA to examining the reasons behind disastrous derailments in India and their solution. Overseas visits also covered areas of engineering development, and these were put to good use on returning home. These were generally adopted by taking a small step at a time: the very essence of good progress which avoids going out on exposed limbs, sometimes with embarrassing results.

Outside railway work on the Government War Effort, he applied his engineering ability in wider areas, which finally took him away to new pastures and into gas turbine engines, production engineering and machine tools.

It may not be realised, but William Stanier had a life-long fascination with machine tools, and this often took him through the machine shops which were manufacturing parts for his locomotives. He always took the opportunity to chat with the machine operators for a first-hand account of how well or otherwise production of the parts was going. He used the same tactic in finding the real situation on locomotive running.

I am delighted to have been asked by the author to write the foreword to such an informative book which has avoided repetition of previously published material, and which gives such an unusual yet delightful mix of family details and happenings.

W.M. (Mike) Stanier,
Duffield, February 2001

Preamble

It was with some considerable trepidation that I commenced to work on this further biography of W.A. Stanier. His life had been covered twice before, by O.S. Nock and H.A.V. Bulleid, yet having read these two masterful accounts I still felt that a further approach was worthwhile. After all, these two hardly mentioned his family background, particularly for the later years, for they had been written before he died. Also, mention of Stanier's extensive overseas journeys was there but only in sparse detail. I felt that if I could locate evidence of these family and travelling events there could well be a further account of an illustrious life with a new approach - the analysis of the man himself.

Starting via my old contacts from earlier biographical accounts (Maunsell and Fowler), I quickly found new material which satisfied my needs and started laying out the book. Soon it was apparent that indeed it was feasible to retell the story with a totally different slant. One factor which gave added impetus was the discovery of a tape recording of an interview with Stanier, in his eighties but still very much all there and obviously only too pleased to talk about his days on the GWR and LMSR.

The result of all the research which provided the new leads is contained herein and I hope that the reader will enjoy this account of a great engineer's life and achievements as much as I did in writing it.

'Princess Royal' class Pacific No. 6206 *Princess Marie Louise* with a down West to North express at Crewe on 13th August, 1935.   *A.W.V. Mace Collection*

Introduction and Acknowledgements

The catalyst for this book was a twofold affair, firstly my involvement in drafting a biography of C.B. Collett, which brought William Stanier into view as an extremely competent engineer. Secondly, having just completed and had published my biography of Sir Henry Fowler, his successor, Stanier, came to mind as a possible further subject. So far I have tried to keep the technical content in my biographies to a sensible amount, after all it is the person in question that provides the main story, the engineering matters covered mainly showing how they dealt with the needs and problems which came under their respective remits.

The two railways involved in this story, the Great Western (GWR) and the London, Midland and Scottish (LMS), were as alike as chalk and cheese in their make-up and approach to motive power considerations for some years after the Grouping in 1923. This aspect was, however, drastically amended once Stanier had moved to Euston from Swindon and began his huge programme of replacing the largely outmoded and obsolescent designs then struggling to maintain a satisfactory service. There were, however, some existing locomotives and project studies for new designs which were deemed to be up to the job. It was these to which Stanier turned as the baselines for some of his range of new designs, plus the addition of types to be based on his GWR experience which were, up to then, alien to the LMS. On all his new designs he ensured that the best of Swindon technology was introduced, although some features did not prove suitable and were amended or discarded.

During the early years of Stanier's reign over 1,200 locomotives were produced to his designs to bring the fleet up-to-date and fully capable of meeting the extreme demands of wartime usage from 1939 onwards. Considering that he only started on the LMS in 1932, the amount of progress made in this huge restocking programme in the 6¾ years available was prodigious, indicating a competent engineer and organiser at work. There were, initially, some minor disappointments but Stanier was willing to learn from experience that not all that was 'standard' at Swindon could necessarily be translated into LMS locomotive design features. He amended his philosophy accordingly to bring about some of the most successful express, mixed traffic and freight engines to grace British rails, some of which were still in quantity production during early Nationalisation days.

I am indebted to Anthony Bulleid for his generous supply of material on Sir William Stanier, whom he knew quite well over the years. In particular for the draft of an extensive article on Stanier the man, which was prepared many years ago for a book which never materialised. I have quoted extensively from this document in my text. Also, and this was quite unique in my own experience of biography writing, he supplied a tape of an interview with Sir William carried out in 1962. From this recording came the many interesting facts which enabled a more complete assessment of a great engineer to be made. All this has enabled me to build a comprehensive picture of Stanier the man and his approach to life on the railways. Other material has been supplied by Jim Jarvis, whose late brother Ron was closely allied to Stanier for many years.

A special vote of thanks must go to Michael Stanier, Sir William's grandson, for the foreword and his generous supply of family material and photographs, as well as such personal data collected by Stanier during his lifetime as still exists. The finding of information such as this enables the biographer to gain a closer insight into his subject. More illustrations came via John Scott-Morgan and Jim Jarvis' extensive photograph collection taken by himself and the late Ron Jarvis.

Two of the appendices to this book are attributed to Stanier himself. Firstly, the report on the Gresley conjugated valve gear commissioned by Edward Thompson is included. This was provided by Anthony Bulleid who has kept the copy originally sent to his father, O.V.S. Bulleid, who had been Gresley's Principal Assistant prior to his CME position on the Southern Railway. Secondly, the draft of the Mitchell Memorial Lecture written and delivered by a 76-year-old Sir William in 1952, which was discovered amongst the family papers kindly lent by his grandson.

I hope that this new biography of a famous locomotive engineer will help in tracing the improvements in locomotive technology which originated in the fertile mind of Stanier's guide and mentor, G.J. Churchward, and how these affected the great programme of change instigated on the LMS just prior to World War II.

Crewe Works 1935. 'Jubilee' class '5XPs' under construction, seen are Nos. 5622 and 5623.
R.S. Carpenter Collection

Chapter One

The Early Days

W.H. Stanier was so well regarded by William Dean, Locomotive Superintendent at the Great Western Railway's works in Wolverhampton, that shortly after Dean's transfer to Swindon to take up the position of Assistant to Joseph Armstrong the Locomotive, Carriage and Wagon Superintendent there, he requested that Stanier accompany him as his chief clerk. W.H. had commenced his employment at Wolverhampton as an office boy and soon made his potential apparent by tackling his simple tasks with keenness and efficiency such that he had been singled out for early promotion, eventually reaching the position of personal clerk to Dean in the early 1870s. Then, in 1877, after his settlement into the job at Swindon, there came the sudden death of Armstrong. The GWR Board appointed Dean to replace the well-respected Armstrong, to begin a quarter of a century of developments including the traumatic days of the broad gauge conversion to the standard gauge. It was not an easy time in which to design and produce new stock for the still expanding railway which by now was no longer wholly broad gauge.

By this date W.H. Stanier had married and the first of his six children, three boys and three girls, had arrived. This first child was a boy, christened William Arthur, born on 27th May, 1876, and who was destined to follow in his father's footsteps into the GWR. This was also the year in which Alexander Graham Bell built his first telephone and the Royal Titles Bill, styling Queen Victoria as Empress of India, was passed through Parliament. Additionally the GWR was preparing to take over the broad gauge South Devon Railway, upon which G.J. Churchward had embarked on a pupilage with John Wright, that line's Locomotive, Carriage and Wagon Superintendent. Churchward was to have a considerable impact on William's career.

William's father was a resourceful man with several additional duties added to his chief clerk's post. Being interested in material quality he had suggested to Dean - and got tacit backing for - the setting up of a testing procedure of mechanical and chemical investigations on samples of incoming materials. Initially this took place at home, but the house was sufficiently spacious for his wife to be amenable to this intrusion. After all, as the years rolled by, she was fully engaged in producing and bringing up the six children. W.H. also took a great interest in the Swindon apprentices and began organising technical education classes for them at Swindon Mechanics Institute.

Young William, probably encouraged by his father, had shown an early interest in matters mechanical. At five years of age he had been discovered experimenting with red hot meat skewers as a means of drilling holes in wood, being suitably admonished and soon diverted from this by his initial schooling at Swindon High School.

By now, the family house, 'Oakfield', The Sands, Swindon was becoming well-filled by the Stanier family. William's mother, never all that robust, had arranged for unmarried Aunt Bessie to come and live there to help out. She was to become a very popular second mother for the children.

Wycliffe College.   *Old Wycliffian Society*

Wycliffe College school group 1893. Somewhere in this group is Charles Stanier, William's
brother.   *Old Wycliffian Society*

At 10 years of age William still enjoyed making things and was presented with his first set of chisels and allocated some workshop space. This was to remain a useful and pleasurable activity, in that order, throughout his life. His interest in sporting matters was to grow from this time. Already an accomplished swimmer, he added tennis and skating as outdoor pursuits, the latter confined to winter months when the Coate reservoir froze over.

In January 1891 his father sent him away as a boarder at Wycliffe College, near Stroud in Gloucestershire, to broaden his education. Wycliffe College had been in existence for some eight years and was gathering a good reputation for its scholastic and sporting successes. Situated close to the stations at Stonehouse, which were served by both the GWR and Midland Railway, it had a total complement of 100 boarders plus 40 day boys in William's time. Although William's showing of academic achievements was unspectacular, the highest placing in Form V being 7th out of 18 for the summer term, his imposing stature and personality had him selected as a Monitor early on. During the Autumn, 1891, Term he sat the Cambridge Local Exams, passing in Preliminaries (Reading, Dictation, Grammar and Arithmetic), Religious Knowledge, English (History, Geography and Shakespeare), French, Algebra and Euclid.

William was to remember this year at Wycliffe for the rest of his days, and in later years was to become President of the Council of Governors. His two brothers were also to attend Wycliffe College, Charles from 1892-95 and James (known as Gordon in the family) from 1897-99.

William returned permanently to Swindon in the 1891 Christmas holidays. His father had arranged for him to be employed as an office boy at Swindon works prior to being taken on as an apprentice at age 16 the following May. He was to commence his many years at Swindon in the Timber Office on the 11th January. The speed at which he completed his many errands was notable and was to be a feature to stay with him throughout his life. The hours were long, 6.00 am to 5.30 pm each day, with a breakfast break (8.15 to 9.00 am) and lunch break (1.00 to 2.00 pm) each day. The total working week was 54 hours, with Saturday finishing at 12 noon. In those days there were no such facilities as works canteens, so William took his meal breaks at his uncle's house which was conveniently close to the works' entrance.

The GWR was about to go through a complete change so far as the gauge was concerned. Brunel's broad gauge, which had never become universal over the whole of the network, was set to be abolished for all time. To the west of the locomotive works and beside the carriage and wagon works, every available square yard of ground was being laid with broad gauge sidings to house the displaced and redundant stock, a proportion of which would be scrapped, with a reasonable amount capable of being converted to the standard gauge. Dean had ensured that much of the broad gauge stock produced under him was of 'convertible' design.

As William Stanier went about his office boy tasks, these sidings gradually filled with withdrawn stock from areas where the track had been converted to mixed gauge and where standard gauge stock was becoming prevalent. By 1892, just 177 miles of dedicated broad gauge remained, all of it on the western extremity of the GWR. The prestige West of England expresses to and from Paddington were still, in the main, run with broad gauge stock until a few weeks

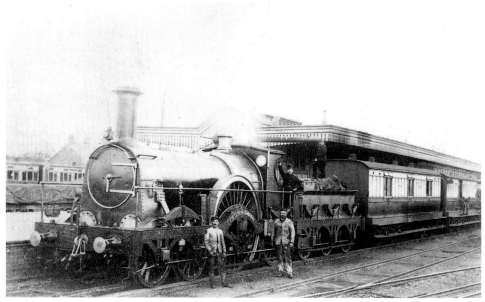

The last broad gauge up mail at Didcot on 20th May, 1892. 'Rover' class locomotive *Bulkeley* which was to haul the last broad gauge express later that day from Paddington, to close an era.
R.S. Carpenter Collection

Broad gauge double-heading. A convertible 2-2-2 pilots a 'Rover' class 4-2-2 at Paddington, 1892.
R.S. Carpenter Collection

Broad gauge sidings, Swindon 1892. A line of 4-2-2s awaits scrapping.

R.S. Carpenter Collection

before the changeover. Young William viewed the last of the broad gauge trains to pass through Swindon (the 5.00 pm from Paddington to the West of England) from a vantage point in the General Offices on the 20th May. This final train was hauled by the 4-2-2 locomotive *Bulkeley*, a Gooch 8-footer with gleaming paintwork and polished brass fittings, which sped past to close an era.

Thus, just a week before his birthday in May, there was a dramatic weekend, planned carefully over the previous months, to convert the remaining stretches of broad gauge to standard gauge. The whole programme was a classic example of splendid organisation and planning of railway working such that the minimum disruption to the running schedules occurred. The difficult part was to ensure that no broad gauge stock was marooned and that Swindon could be reached for scrapping or conversion.

The conversion plan was included in a 50-page instruction document prepared by the staff of the General Manager together with a further 30 pages extra for the Bristol and Exeter superintendents. Some 4,200 platelayers and gangers were collected and transported from all over the railway and in a space of 30 hours, on the 21st/22nd May, 1892, with the expenditure of almost one million pounds, the broad gauge was no more. Brunel's dream had gone.

William would have seen his father at work only occasionally in his days as office boy and in the early years of his apprenticeship, for W.H. had been promoted from his chief clerk's job to Stores Superintendent early in 1892. One wonders if William was ever accorded the traditional apprentice task of being sent to the stores for a left-handed spanner. The temptation for his workmates would have been there, but the knowledge of his father's position and accord with William Dean probably kept them from trying that one on!

The week following his 16th birthday, William was dispatched to the carriage works, where he found himself placed in the saw mill, preparing timber for the eventual transformation into new carriage stock and also for the conversion of the old broad gauge stock. He spent some 19 months in these works, finishing off in the fitting shop in late 1893, having covered all the main areas of carriage construction. His early childhood days of getting familiar with woodworking at home would have given him a good start when it came to the simple tasks initially accorded him.

In November of that year his transfer to the locomotive works on the north side of the London-Bristol line came through, this time a 21 month placement to

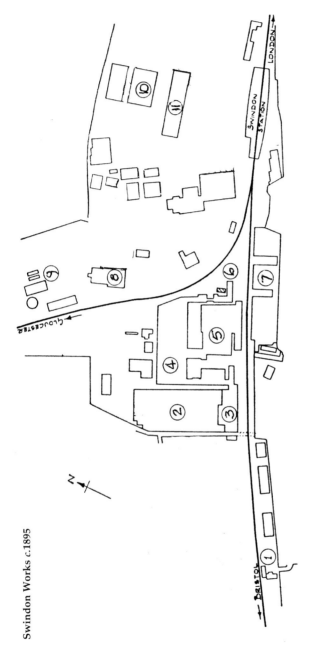

Swindon Works c.1895

Key

1. Newburn
2. Boiler shop
3. Iron foundry
4. Rolling mill
5. Machine and erecting shop
6. Offices

7. Carriage shops
8. Running shed
9. Gas works
10. Carriage lifting
11. Wagon lifting

Author

the fitting and machine shops. The change of material in the fitting shop taught him new skills in managing metal components, whilst the machine shop immediately had an impact on him. He was to take a great interest in machine tool development in later years, particularly when the shaft and belt driven machines were given individual electric drives in the modernization to come in the 20th century. This also, more importantly, was to become a life-long speciality, particularly in his time in the works management offices as well as in Government service in later life.

With a good grounding in the manufacture of detail components for both carriages and locomotives, in mid-1895 a shift to the erecting shop was ordered. Under construction were batches of 2-4-0 tanks for the Metropolitan services around London, plus a new batch of Dean's 4-2-2s for top express services. It was with these new locomotives that he enjoyed one of the apprentice's few perks, that of accompanying an engine on its first trial run after construction or repair. Also the beginning of a standardisation policy was becoming visible as the works strove to keep production costs down. Four months on new engines was followed by a further four months on the repair of engines.

In May 1896 came a move to the millwright's shop where for six months his main tasks were participating in fitting and erecting steam and hand cranes used for emergency work throughout the GWR. The final six months of his apprenticeship were spent in the pattern shop.

During this time of long hours coupled with strict discipline, much of his spare time was taken up with attendance at the Mechanics Institute for the night classes in engineering subjects, available to all apprentices should they wish to consider entering the design area. He acquitted himself well here, showing a natural aptitude for assessing technical subjects in some detail.

The final Certificate of Apprenticeship given to William had a telling paragraph on his time in the works:

> William A. Stanier has satisfactorily completed a term of 5 years apprenticeship at these Works, as shewn above. He has always borne a very good character, has been punctual and diligent in attention to his duties and the foremen under whom he has been employed report that he is a very good workman.
>
> sgnd Wm Dean
> Chief Superintendent
> GWR Loco & Carr Department.

In May 1897, having completed the formal part of his training, and having found an interest in detail design via the pattern shop, he spent six months as a fully-fledged pattern maker employee (this was in the days before Trade Union membership was to become obligatory). He accepted, after some contratemps with the foreman as to his abilities, a starting rate of 22s. per week. This compared to the 24s. starting rate normally given to a pattern maker and indicated the foreman's natural reluctance to accept that an engineering apprentice could possibly have acquired the skills necessary during his brief few months in the shop.

On the 1st November of that year, he moved out of the works environment to the Drawing Office, where he was given a junior draughtsman's job in the carriage and wagon section. The technical ladder had been reached and the first decisive step taken on the long climb to the top.

GREAT WESTERN RAILWAY.

LOCOMOTIVE & CARRIAGE DEPARTMENT,
ENGINEER'S OFFICE,

18141/a

SWINDON, 15th June 1897.

Certificate of Apprenticeship.

Name William A. Stanier

Period of Apprenticeship 5 years from 27th May 1892 to 26th May 1897.

Where employed Locomotive & Carriage Works, Swindon.

Work on which employed

		Months
Carriage Works.		
Saw Mill	Fitting	19
Locomotive Works		
General Fitting & Machine Shop	Fitting and Turning	21
Erecting Shop	Erecting new engines	4
" "	General Repairs	4
Millwrights' Shop	Fitting & Erecting Steam & Hand Cranes	6
Pattern Making Shop	General Pattern Making	6
		60 = 5 years

YEAR ENDED		HOURS WORKS OPEN.	HOURS WORKED	TIME LOST (HOURS) SPECIAL LEAVE	ILLNESS	WITHOUT LEAVE	TOTAL	
May	1893	2303¼	2258¼	40½	-	4½	45	
"	1894	2638½	2341½	192	93¾	11¼	297	
"	1895	2560½	2384¾	80½	93	2¼	175¾	
"	1896	2522½	2477¾	41¾	-	3	44¾	
"	1897	2633¼	2439½	123½	62¾	6¼ 7½	193¾	
TOTALS ...		12,658	*11,901¾	478¼	249½	28½	756¼	* Includes 27¼ hours overtime.

N.B.—The "Hours Works open" does not include the Works Holiday (averaging about 20 days per annum); "Special leave" represents time lost for Holidays in addition to the usual Works Holidays.

William A Stanier has satisfactorily completed a term of 5 years apprenticeship at these Works, as shewn above. He has always borne a very good character, has been punctual and diligent in attention to his duties, and the foremen under whom he has been employed report that he is a very good workman.

Wm Dean
Chief Superintendent
G.W.R. Loco. & Carr. Department

H.J.

Certificate of Apprenticeship. *W.M. Stanier*

Chapter Two

Design and Other Experiences

Two years and five months were spent in the drawing offices in total, with a switch to the Locomotive Drawing Office coming on 9th January, 1899. Here William was to be involved in both the locomotive and experimental sections. The recently appointed assistant chief draughtsman, C.B. Collett, soon noticed the abilities of William as a competent draughtsman.

William Dean still occupied the Locomotive, Carriage and Wagon Superintendent's position, with Churchward as principal assistant in addition to his Works Manager responsibilities, but his health was giving rise for concern and Churchward was, with the Board's quiet backing, tending to make the running in design matters.

One job put William's way in the experimental section was the design of the underframe for a new GWR dynamometer car. Built into this was a G.H. Pearson design for a special transmission spring which was virtually free of hysteresis, having rollers placed between the leaves. Smoother recording of drawbar pulls was possible with this logical development. Pearson was later to be enticed to the South Eastern & Chatham Railway (SE&CR) under R.E.L. Maunsell to take up the position of Works Manager at the Ashford works and to remain as such into Southern Railway days.

News of Stanier's good handling of the tasks accorded him soon filtered through to Dean and Churchward. Therefore, on 1st March, 1900, he was appointed inspector of materials - a position not unfamiliar with the Stanier name at Swindon itself - but this posting was associated with the Birmingham and Manchester Districts of the GWR.

His technical education having finished with the end of his apprenticeship and by now having acquired a reasonable all-round experience on the design and technical side of matters, William, at the age of 25, applied for Associate Membership of the Institution of Mechanical Engineers, being proposed by Dean and seconded by Churchward, James Holden, F.G. Wright and H.C. King. The application was dated 1st July, 1901 and approved shortly after. With this first major technical qualification and his obvious competence, a further move was inevitable as he was, by now, clearly being honed for future high office.

This next promotion took place in September 1901 following one of Dean's casual meetings with Stanier's father. After commiserating with W.H. Stanier on his recent defeat in the local council election, he asked about William's progress and position. Dean then indicated his intention of placing him as a mechanical inspector at Swindon Loco. This was a key posting at which his abilities would be tried to the extreme. He would be working under the Divisional Locomotive Superintendent, W.H. Willams. Swindon Shed, at that time, stabled some 40 passenger and 60 goods locomotives and the divisional management also controlled the Gloucester, Severn and Wye, Oxford, Reading, Trowbridge and Weymouth sheds. Once settled into this new job, William would sometimes be dispatched to one of these sheds as a relief foreman, giving him a feel for running his own show. It was all good experience for future years.

I.Mech.E. application form for membership.   *I.Mech.E.*

Westbourne Park Shed. Two years after this was taken, Stanier was in charge here. The locomotive in view is 'Atbara' class No. 3374 renamed *Kitchener* for Kitchener special run on 12th July, 1902.   *J. Scott-Morgan Collection*

One feature of William's upbringing and education had been the instilling into him of the need to enforce strict discipline when leading others. This became apparent in the case of 3rd class engineman J.H. Thomas, who was found smoking when on duty - which was strictly forbidden - and reprimanded by William for setting a bad example to those under him. A little over a year after his arrival at Swindon, William was promoted from his mechanical inspector's post to that of Assistant Divisional Locomotive Superintendent there.

Having shown himself fully capable of managing matters at Swindon, William was promoted yet again, the new job being the Assistant Divisional Superintendent at the Westbourne Park shed just outside Paddington, where he commenced on 11th January, 1904. Together with this placement came a rise to annual staff status.

The Westbourne Park job only went to those who were competent, energetic and a good disciplinarian. It was also a good vantage point from which William saw the start of Churchward's massive programme for re-equipping the GWR with his range of standard engines. It was an experience which was to be repeated for him in the 1930s on the LMS. Having been on the receiving end at Westbourne Park must have eased William's approach to matters in those later years.

The footplate staff at Westbourne were encouraged to attend the Mutual Improvement Classes and Stanier often could be found speaking at these. A series of his lectures concerned the differences between the Stephenson and the recently introduced Walschaerts valve gears and their respective effects on locomotive handling. He also took some evening classes for drivers and firemen at Willesden Technical College to increase their theoretical information on the steam locomotive and its handling. William let his pupils know that his own experiences, whilst not up to their standards, were still adequate enough to demonstrate some of the points he put over.

Visits back to Swindon were quite frequent, for two reasons, firstly he was still a key member of the Town's water-polo team and, secondly, he was courting a Swindon girl, Ella Elizabeth (Nelle) Morse. This latter reason became steadily more of a priority until, in 1905, they became engaged. Nelle was the elder daughter of Mr L.L. Morse, JP, of The Croft, Swindon, who was to be the Member of Parliament for the North Wiltshire Division.

One new locomotive to arrive at Westbourne Park had been No. 171, Churchward's second 4-6-0, which had been converted to a 4-4-2 for a strict comparison with the French compound Atlantic being tried out in the search for a definitive design to standardise on. Following the initial trials of No. 171 a further batch of similar 4-4-2s were built and put into service. For some inexplicable reason these were poor steamers and one day in 1905 when Churchward was at Paddington, he sent for Stanier to discuss this shortcoming. William mentioned that No. 171 had a different ashpan design to the new batch, with dampers each side in addition to the normal front and back dampers. He stated that the air under the grate could be limited by lack of adequate damper area. 'Dammit, Stanier,' exclaimed Churchward, 'I think you're right.' The engines were modified with the extra dampers and the problem disappeared.

French 4-4-2 No. 104 *Alliance* as rebuilt with standard boiler in 1908. Caught at Paddington.

R.S. Carpenter Collection

No. 171 *Albion*, the first Churchward Atlantic, converted from the original 4-6-0, on a down express near Friars Junction, Acton. *c.*1904-05.   *J. Scott-Morgan Collection*

William and Nelle and engagement photograph.   *W.M. Stanier*

An official wedding photograph of William and Nelle.   *W.M. Stanier*

The work at Westbourne Park became more hectic, with much to do on the new engines and the planning of the move to the new shed then being erected at Old Oak Common, just a short distance down the main line. The old facilities were getting decidedly cramped with the introduction of 4-6-0s in place of 4-4-0s and also the increase in traffic.

It was therefore with some relief that William received notice of his transfer back to Swindon in April 1906, for the wedding was set for July and the salary increase, although small, was most welcome at such a time. The new position was as assistant to H.C. King, the Works Manager, but was only a holding operation for some six months, for in November came a further promotion, to the position of Divisional Locomotive, Carriage and Wagon Superintendent at Swindon, at a salary of £500 (£50,000 in today's terms). The newly-weds set up home at 'Walden', Westlecot Road, Swindon, and William began to prepare for the greater responsibility accorded him.

Whether or not Stanier knew of the 'Saint' trial of speed in May 1906 has never been revealed, but it seems quite likely that news of the event filtered through to him in the Works Manager's Department as he waited for the transfer to Swindon Loco.

It appears that someone had made the comment that it should be possible to take an engine straight from the works and, on the test run, achieve a speed of over 100 mph. Whilst the Great Western regularly achieved speeds of 80 mph on express services, and sometimes 90 mph for short periods, the magic figure of 100 mph had been taken as a target. Churchward, one is fairly sure, was not put in the picture - he would most certainly have vetoed it. Accordingly, No. 2903 *Lady of Lyon*, fresh from the shops was taken on the usual test run as a light engine prior to entering traffic.

It transpired that on the return to Swindon, down the nine miles of 1 in 300 from Little Somerford, the engine was opened out and achieved a reported speed of 120 mph. Collett was one of the four on the footplate and in 1932 'came clean' about the incident, admitting some stopwatch timings between mileposts were taken, giving the 120 mph. Clearly the engine had been pushed to its limits and with the free-running characteristics of the Churchward design the speed could certainly have risen to a three-figure value. William was busy preparing for his forthcoming marriage and the incident probably passed him by. He never was known to comment on the event in later years.

The importance of Swindon Loco, in particular around this time, was that the trials' enginemen ran all the new engines as they came off works, with the mechanical inspectors following up their performance. Stanier naturally rode on and drove many of them and was involved in shed/works arguments, and so got the shrewdest possible look at all the new Churchward designs including the *Great Bear* in 1908. In April of that year he applied for transfer to Member of the I.Mech.E., with Churchward writing a succinct and telling note in support: 'Mr W.A. Stanier is the Divisional Superintendent of our Swindon Division, which is one of the most important on the railway. He is a well-educated and able Engineer and I think well qualified to be transferred to the class of Member'.

This was duly endorsed by the President, T. Hurry Riches of the Taff Vale Railway.

The Churchward 4-6-0 'Saint' class.   *I.Mech.E.*

No. 180 *Coeur de Lion* built as a 4-4-2 leaves Bristol on a Paddington express, *c.*1907-08.
                                                              R.S. Carpenter Collection

It had been in 1906 that Churchward saw particulars in the American technical press of what was called the American semi-plug piston valve. He was so impressed with the design that he purchased the rights of manufacture in the UK and also obtained a pair of valves for trial on the GWR. The design of these valves was such that the rings for maintaining steam tightness were expanded by steam pressure when the regulator was open and thus fitted the walls of the valve chest and were locked in position by means of locking rings also actuated by steam pressure. When steam was shut off the rings were not in contact with the valve chest walls so that there was practically no wear when drifting, giving a very free running engine.

The manufacture and fitting of these valves was expensive, involving a lot of hand finishing. Stanier had much to do with the initial trials of these valves in his Divisional Superintendent's position and eventually some machining processes were developed which eliminated the costly hand finishing. This process was always carried out at Swindon works and it was to remain exclusively a GWR speciality.

It was around this time that it came to the notice of Churchward that Aspinall, on the Lancashire & Yorkshire Railway had introduced a punched card system to compile data from the drivers' daily returns. Interested in this, he dispatched Stanier on a visit to Horwich to investigate. William was met at Bolton station and sped to Horwich in the CME's coupé. Upon his return from this VIP treatment he said he was flattered to be taken in the coupé, but it rode worse than anything on the GWR. This pleased his assistant, R.J. Armstrong (the last of the GWR Armstrongs), who later characterised Stanier as a broad-minded and far-seeing man who did not suffer from what was termed the 'Swindon Complex'.

The task of supervising the important Swindon motive power scene encompassed a wide range of responsibilities, one of which was the inauguration, on the Oxford-Fairford branch, of Automatic Train Control (ATC), which was later to be extended to all the major routes of the GWR. With the signals remaining the driver's instruction, the fail-safe aspect of the warning system ensured that, if ignored, it applied the brakes, making it impossible for a train to pass the stop signal beyond the distant signal at which the warning was given. The trials proved the efficiency of ATC which then began to be installed on the main lines, starting with the section between Paddington and Reading.

Outside of the work environment, William's activities included a series of papers on locomotive design and operation given to the Swindon Engineering Society. This organisation was affiliated to the GWR Mechanics Institution. By 1911, he was Chairman of the Engineering Society. At home, the arrival of a son (William) and a daughter (Joan) kept Nelle busy and 'Oakfield' once again resounded to the sound of children's fun and games on the family's visits to his parents.

Churchward was an excellent design leader, in that he kept the overall picture of motive power needs in his mind. This was helped by regular 3-monthly meetings with all the chiefs of works and running staffs. Usually one would find Locomotive, Carriage and Wagon Works Managers, the Running Superintendent and the eight Divisional Superintendents at these meetings, often with their respective deputies in tow. Around 1910 it became apparant that a design of locomotive was needed which was capable of tackling goods traffic, but also with adequate speed and acceleration to cope with passenger traffic. And so was born the 'mixed traffic' 2-6-0.

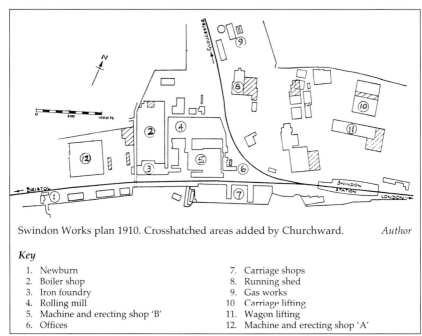

Swindon Works plan 1910. Crosshatched areas added by Churchward.   *Author*

Key

1.	Newburn	7.	Carriage shops
2.	Boiler shop	8.	Running shed
3.	Iron foundry	9.	Gas works
4.	Rolling mill	10.	Carriage lifting
5.	Machine and erecting shop 'B'	11.	Wagon lifting
6.	Offices	12.	Machine and erecting shop 'A'

Stanier was fully in accord with this directive and in 1911 the first of a batch of 20 appeared at Swindon shed for running in. There were no prototypes, the design being a clever amalgam of standard parts from Churchward's standardisation policy.

The new mixed traffic design, the '4300' class, proved popular from the start, being received by the Divisions as a most useful addition to the range of standard types. There was, however, one slight criticism regarding the cramped access to the injectors and brake gear beneath the footplate. Following this the remainder of this class and its successors had the rear overhang increased by nine inches and the slightly longer '3801' class (the 4-4-0 'County') cab was adopted.

William acquired a new relative in 1912, when James Milne married Nelle's younger sister. Milne had started on the GWR as a pupil of Churchward in 1903, being transferred to the Traffic Department in London in 1908, following which he was placed in the General Manager's office. The year he married he was promoted to Head of the Passenger Train Running Department under the Superintendent of the Line. From here he was to hold a series of appointments leading to his promotion to General Manager in 1929 after the resignation of Sir Felix Pole.

As 1912 drew to a close, Stanier was told of his next promotion, to the position of Assistant (Senior) Locomotive Works Manager, H.C. King the Works Manager having been elevated to Assistant to Churchward, and his position filled by C.B. Collett. The job became official from 1st January, 1913 and the new Works Manager and his Assistant were given full encouragement to improve and modernise the works. They were to work together for the next two decades. With this job came a move to a company house, No. 1, Church Place, just down the road from Charles Collett at No. 5.

Chapter Three

The Works Days

One of the first tasks delegated to Stanier by Collett was that of improving the productivity and accuracy in the machine shops. Much of the improvements were aimed at achieving reduced fitting operations due to improved tolerances. This raised some objections and one chargehand, in a plea to retain hand scraping of journals, said it improved lubrication by leaving some valleys to retain oil. Stanier promptly replied, 'Yes, and some mountain peaks to break the oil film.' William's speed during his tours of inspection, coupled to his very dark hair, soon earned him the nickname of 'The Black Arrow' within the works. This feature will reappear throughout the book, even into the latter years when most people slow down and become more relaxed.

Conditions in the works were at a rather critical stage, for there had been a trade recession affecting the whole country and Churchward's policy of standardisation had produced an increase in the running times between repairs and more standardised parts had reduced the stores holdings. Short time working caused by all these factors had resulted in the need for redundancies. To compound all this, there was a National Coal Strike in March 1912 causing a large reduction in railway business and reductions in services to conserve stocks. This again brought more pressure for short time working. Outside of Stanier's remit, but still affecting his position as Assistant Works Manager, was the introduction in 1913 of electric clocks in every shop, working on the 'Magenta' master and slave clock system. Although installed to provide time information to meet the requirements of the Railway Accounts Bill, introduced in 1911, they proved the catalyst for the Trades Unions to complain that individuals' times would be gauged on this system. They argued that a measure of 'slave-driving' would occur, with the jobs being timed on the speed of the fastest worker. However, talks with the union representatives (there were now some 1,500 union members at Swindon) managed to convince them that, ultimately, a more rigorous time measuring system would benefit the works as a whole by improving work efficiency and controlling costs. However, the Unions had flexed their muscles and a long battle on pay and conditions was set to commence.

However, William was only in his new job a little over 18 months when war broke out, on 4th August, 1914. It had been anticipated for some time, and in concert with the other railways, the GWR began to plan for wartime production needs. The 'A' shop expansion plans, formulated in 1912 and sanctioned by the Board (£165,000 for buildings and £20,000 for equipment) were immediately put on hold for the duration. On that day in August the works hooter sounded 10 long blasts, a prearranged signal to the town that hostilities had commenced and that reservists should prepare to muster. Many of these reservists were from the GWR works and during the following few days Stanier and Collett were busy with the foremen assessing the employee situation. For although the GWR's own production would be curtailed somewhat, the needs of the war would make considerable demands on the capacity available.

Stanier concentrated on finishing off his modernisation plans, which were to pay off handsomely during the war. His updating of the machine shop showed that there was hardly any task they could not meet, even to rifling gun barrels. He was now 38, too old to enlist, and felt deeply that he owed it to colleagues overseas to spare no effort that might help them.

Collett, on the other hand, was most upset that much of the works effort was to be for war work at the expense of skimping on locomotive maintenance. He could forsee problems ahead with inadequately serviced locomotives affecting services, and this indeed was eventually to be a major worry as hostilities continued.

Just before war broke out, William had gone to Paris for the I.Mech.E. July summer meeting where six papers on cab signals used for train control were presented. He followed Aspinall and Fowler in the discussion, saying of the GWR system: 'When I was in charge of the engines working over the Fairford branch, all the drivers reported that the arrangement gave every satisfaction'. Aspinall had made some pertinent points and in reply to these William said: 'I think Mr Aspinall's requirements for the audible signal gear are exactly covered by the Great Western system. Mr Aspinall's argument that an irresponsible wireman was trusted to make good the electric contacts was to a certain extent overcome, at any rate on the side of safety, by the audible signal device at the slightest failure of energy'. In fact, in the early days of the GWR system some instances of cross-wiring had occurred, but once discovered had been circumvented by fitting different sized terminal connectors to the wires. When asked in later years whether the enginemen themselves had ever interfered with the ATC equipment on the engines, Stanier's reply was short and decisive: 'No, never.'

The interest aroused by the summer meeting, plus the fact that ATC on the GWR was now set for future expansion to all major routes, spurred the I.Mech.E. to arrange a symposium in December 1914 on 'Audible and Other Cab Signals'. This had five papers offered on the subject, with Vincent Raven giving one on behalf of the North Eastern Railway and Stanier for the GWR.

After giving a description of the GWR ATC system, Stanier mentioned that recently a visiting USA Commission had reported that only the GWR system seemed 'worthy of further consideration'. In the discussion that ensued he showed himself fully capable of answering any technical criticism plus not being afraid of promoting the GWR philosophy. He returned to Swindon, after this maiden appearance as a contributor to a well-respected Institution, to buckle down to the many problems in the works as munitions work and the associated re-tooling started to take precedence. Although some had said the war would be over by the New Year, it was now obvious the country was in for a long and exhausting campaign.

The war work of Swindon has been well-documented elsewhere and will not be covered in any great detail save that, despite the considerable loss of skilled men to the colours following the call for volunteers, no slackening in output occurred. (2,634 Swindon men had answered the call within the first two months of conflict, a very large percentage of these must have been railwaymen.)

A few relevant points are worth recording. The facilities at Swindon attracted orders from the War Office, Ministry of Munitions, Woolwich Arsenal, the Admiralty and, as sub-contractors, many other private companies engaged in war work. Stanier and Collett were busy in the planning of shop layouts to permit the installation of extra machine tools needed for the specialised work involved. Many of these machines were bought by the GWR and charged to the Government account.

Soon after Henry Fowler, CME of the Midland Railway, had been appointed as Director of Production for the Ministry of Munitions, he was at a meeting with Churchward at which he was impressing on him the urgency behind many of the needs facing the Ministry's procurement plans. As the discussion progressed, Fowler nonchalantly produced a fuse for a 2 inch shell turned out at the Midland Railway (MR) works at Derby, indicating that at least 3,000 were required each week. Churchward returned hurriedly to Swindon at the close of the meeting and called in Stanier to ask why could they not turn out fuses at that rate. William was rather taken aback by this blunt approach and countered it by stating that of course they could manufacture that number, but only if space were allocated and the machines set up and manned. Churchward then agreed that part of the cylinder shop might be converted and equipped for fuse manufacture, following which Swindon duly turned out 3,000 a week.

So far as locomotives were concerned, 100, all 0-6-0s, were dispatched overseas, made up of 22 Armstrong class '388' and 78 Dean class '2301'. Of this total eight were lost in transit and 11 never returned after the war. Several had been considerably modified to accommodate a Westinghouse brake system, extended cab roof and pannier tanks to augment the tender water supply. The shortfall in stock was made up by the continued production of the 2-6-0, some 120 being built during the 1914-18 period.

As the war progressed, William's father, who had been at Paddington some time now, retired in 1916 following a long and successful career on the GWR and as a contributor in the public life of Swindon and elsewhere. The family name, however, was destined to remain with the GWR for some time yet as William continued to make his mark. Churchward, who had accepted the change of his title to that of Chief Mechanical Engineer in 1916, was much involved in the latter years of the war with the Design Committee set up by the Association of Railway Locomotive Engineers (ARLE) to design a series of standard locomotives should the mooted nationalisation take place after the war. He was now in his early sixties and retirement was within his sight. Once hostilities had ceased, some moves to reorganise the top people at Swindon would be made, for on Churchward's departure a move up through the ranks would follow.

If the GWR followed precedent, it would be Collett who would move into the CME's shoes. Collett was Stanier's senior by only five years, but the railway habit of bowing to age seniority almost certainly meant he would be in line for the job.

William had found Collett a very capable superior, maybe a little detached, but then he was, outside the works environment, very much attached to his wife and his private life was just that, private. Their teamwork through the war years had been exemplary, which boded well for the future.

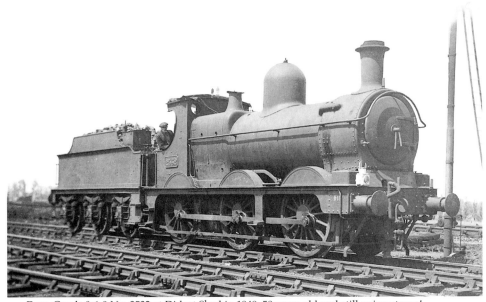

Dean Goods 0-6-0 No. 2532 at Didcot Shed in 1949. 50 years old and still going strong!

R.S. Carpenter Collection

Dean Goods No. 2572 on a local passenger turn at Saltney Junction *c.*1936.

A.V.W. Mace Collection

Hostilities ceased on 11th November, 1918 and the railways began to survey the state of their stock, track and systems, which all needed urgent attention. In 1919 Churchward started planning the changes at the top. He was, to put it mildly, a little dismayed by the radical changes in labour relations coming into play. Stanier and Collett, however, had been closer to such events and were fully conversant in the ways and means to handle the new relationships with the now more powerful and influential Unions.

Therefore, in 1920, William found himself promoted to Works Manager, Collett having been elevated to Assistant to the CME in preparation for his by now inevitable move into that job. Churchward was now indicating that he would like to retire at the end of 1921. 'It is' he is reputed to have said, 'time for the Old Man to go.'

The Swindon Works Manager had, traditionally, always been a tough job, demanding constant attention to day-to-day discipline, progress, costs, and what is now called house-keeping. Swindon's enviable reputation was only maintained by constant vigilance. Accordingly the line of Works Managers had tended to be on the austere side, giving crisp but fair instructions and expecting action without argument. Stanier entirely fitted the pattern; his tall and commanding presence, on the dark side with his very dark hair and moustache, and his decided lack of verbosity, ranked him quite fairly as austere and taciturn - while on the job. At home, or helping someone in trouble, he was relaxed and friendly and usually ready with an encouraging remark. He was devoted to his family and took a lasting interest in his three nieces and four nephews, to whom he was known as Uncle Will, provided by his brothers Charles (an engineer with the District Railway) and Gordon (a solicitor) and they could always count on handsome Christmas presents. He had kept his home workshop going, practising what he preached with all his tools in mint condition and neatly stamped 'W A STANIER' thanks to a steel punch made in the tool room.

In his spare time, William kept himself up-to-date with improvements in locomotive design. Churchward actively encouraging this as he himself had adopted many of his technical advances from such an approach. One feature which appeared in 1919, when the '4700' class 2-8-0 was being designed, was the outside steam pipe, which was actively promoted by William. This gave a more direct passage of steam from the regulator to the steam chest, thus giving lower losses in pressure and flow. The prototype did not have this 'novel idea' as Churchward was recorded as saying, for the boiler assembly initially fitted, being a standard No. 1, did not have outside steampipes. The definitive boiler, the new No. 7, fitted to the production batch of this class was designed from the start with this distinctive feature, which was to become a standard for all future outside cylinder designs to emanate from Swindon, and also on many other railways as they saw the distinct benefit to performance available.

Just prior to Churchward's departure it was known that the railways were to be grouped as specified in the Railways Act, this becoming effective from the 1st January, 1923. The GWR was to be the least affected of the four grouped railways, only being joined to a number of the small South and Mid Wales lines with their rather specialised needs. Swindon, clearly, was still going to be the prime site for production and major maintenance and so matters there would be virtually unchanged.

Joan Stanier (daughter) at about 8 years.   *W.M. Stanier*

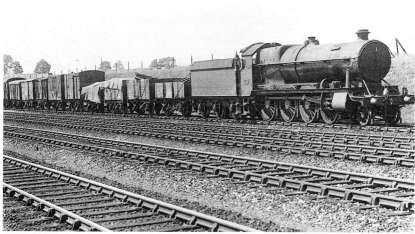

GWR '4700' class 2-8-0 on mixed freight near Reading *c*.1940.

J. Scott-Morgan Collection

Before the publication of the Railways Act, Churchward had received approval from the Board to continue his expansion of 'A' Shop, curtailed by the war. So, as Stanier moved to Works Manager he found himself in the thick of a major expansion programme which, upon completion, had cost some £440,000 (equivalent today to something in the region of £30 million). When finished, Swindon was the most up-to-date railway works in the UK and had a productive capacity of at least 100 new locomotives per year, in addition to the repairs to a fleet of some 4,000. However, William was only destined to be Works Manager until shortly after Grouping had commenced, for Collett, in his first year in charge as CME, took his time in building his team and was to offer the position of Assistant to the CME to his former assistant and colleague of works days.

And so began a further decade of close teamwork, this time covering the design side of matters.

G.J. Churchward, a portrait near to retirement of a great locomotive engineer.   *W.M. Stanier*

Chapter Four

Swindon after Grouping

Churchward had provided the GWR with a range of standard locomotives so advanced that there was little to do as regards design changes in new developments. Where new types were concerned, only in the context of styling changes did Collett and Stanier have to involve the locomotive draughtsmen, who were a well-balanced and experienced team under G.H. Burrows the chief draughtsman. They were, mainly, just content to make minor improvements where possible to the well-balanced technical expertise of Churchward.

As William started on his Principal Assistant rôle, he was taken aside by Collett one day and told firmly to let the new Works Manager, R.A.G. Hannington, stand on his own feet. The immediate task for the CME's office was to assess the situation as regards all the Welsh valley railways then being amalgamated under Grouping, and Stanier helped Collett to listen patiently to their needs. One result was the special design of '5600' class 0-6-2 tanks for them, another was the concentration of locomotive repair work in those parts by extending the Rhymney works at Caerphilly and closing the Taff Vale works at Cardiff.

After Grouping Collett concentrated on finishing off the outstanding order for eight '4700' class mixed-traffic 2-8-0s and authorised the construction of 12 'Star' class 4-6-0s to bring the fleet total of that successful 4-cylinder type up to 73.

The new 'Stars' were only ever seen as a stop-gap until something more substantial could be provided. Design work was commencing on the 4-cylinder 'Castle' class 4-6-0, upon which Collett was to stamp his authority in the restyling of the cab from the rather spartan and skimpy Churchward design to his own side-window version with a generous roof overhang.

However, Stanier found himself with much on his plate in March 1923 when Collett's wife died quite suddenly after a short illness. Collett had been very close to her, his whole life outside work revolved around her, and he took this loss very hard indeed. At times it seemed as if his hold on life was slipping, so the responsibilities on William's shoulders were great for some months. Collett, always a withdrawn man socially, required careful and considerate handling in the office and the pressure to complete the 'Castle' design was largely devolved on William. He was, however, quite capable of taking the strain and the new locomotive's scheming proceeded with the prototype *Caerphilly Castle* appearing in July 1923, being proudly proclaimed by the GWR Publicity Department as 'The most powerful express locomotive in the UK'.

The success of this new express type was underlined on 28th April, 1924 when King George V and Queen Mary paid the first official Royal Visit to the town of Swindon. After the civic part of the visit ended, the Royal party arrived at the GWR works entrance for a guided tour of the facilities. Collett, who had recovered sufficiently from the loss of his wife, had been the works representative for the civic tour (he was, after all, a JP in Swindon), and Stanier were in the party awaiting the distinguished guests, and the latter was to help conduct them through the locomotive works.

'5600' class 0-6-2T at Chester 10th April, 1938.   *R.S. Carpenter Collection*

'Star' class 4-6-0 No. 4005 *Polar Star* at Old Oak Common. May 1934.   *R.S. Carpenter Collection*

No. 4023 *The Danish Monarch* on down express of LMS stock, pulling hard up to Dainton tunnel in the late 1930s. *J. Scott-Morgan Collection*

'Castle' class 4-6-0 No. 4076 *Carmarthen Castle* of the first production batch, prepares to leave Paddington. July 1925. *R.S. Carpenter Collection*

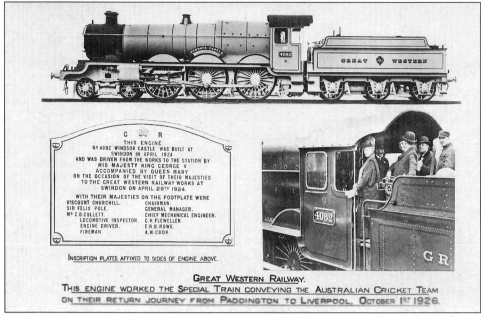

A period picture postcard depicting 'Castle' class No. 4082 *Windsor Castle* on the occasion of the Royal Tour of Swindon 1924.

J. Alsop Collection

'Castle' class No. 5000 *Launceston Castle,* of the 1926-7 batch, some of which had the 4,000 gallon tender as depicted here in the 1930s.

J. Scott-Morgan Collection

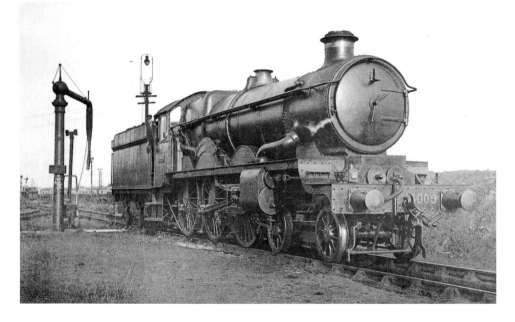

The guests arrived at the Sheppard Street entrance of the carriage works, where the tour was to commence. Following their inspection they then crossed the main line to the locomotive works to be met by the manager, Hannington. Stanier and Hannington then conducted the distinguished guests around; they saw, among other things, a '4300' class locomotive running at full speed on the test plant and a complete engine being lifted and moved by one of the four 100 ton overhead cranes.

Following this tour of the works the Royal Party proceeded to the Royal Train with, appropriately, No. 4082 *Windsor Castle* attached. The King and Queen were invited by Sir Felix Pole onto the footplate, for the King to 'drive' the train the short distance to Swindon station where they entrained for the remainder of the return journey to London. The GWR Publicity Department made much of the event, further promoting the advent of the 'Castle' class.

After Grouping, the ARLE was considerably reduced in numbers as many of the CMEs of the constituent railways making up the four main lines had been retired or moved to rather lower posts. Prior to 1923, a Rules Committee had been set up to decide who should be eligible for membership of this unique body. Basically, what had been decided by this forum was that all CMEs, C&W Superintendents and Deputy CMEs/Principal Assistants should automatically qualify, subject to a maximum of six members from any railway. Collett remained the sole member representing the GWR until January 1926, when Stanier was present for the first time, having been proposed for membership under the Principal Assistant ruling.

The undoubted success of the 'Castles' was not the end of matters concerned with the express fleet, with Collett and Stanier not reclining on this. The GWR Civil Engineering Department had brought about some bridge improvements permitting higher axle loads, and with the Southern Railway having usurped the ownership of 'Britain's most powerful express locomotive' with Maunsell's 'Lord Nelson' Collett went beyond the Churchward design parameters for the first time and designed the 'King' class. Stanier got Hannington to mount an all-out effort to complete *King George V* in time for its shipping, on 3rd August, 1927, to the USA to take part in the Baltimore and Ohio Railroad (B&ORR) Centenary celebrations. They just managed, and the brand-new engine's only rehearsal was to work the 'Cornish Riviera Express' for a few days starting on 20th July. A few days earlier Sir Henry Fowler had taken Gresley and Stanier to see the brand-new *Royal Scot* at Euston, and introduced it as 'the finest engine in the British Isles'. 'Or, anyway, the finest smokebox', Stanier could not help remarking, with the advantage of having just seen the new 'King'.

To accompany the 'King', it was decided to send a broad gauge replica to represent those unique days of the early GWR nearly 90 years previously. The original *North Star*, the first locomotive to haul a passenger train on the GWR, had lain in Swindon works carefully preserved until Churchward for some reason ordered its scrapping along with another broad gauge locomotive, the *Lord of the Isles* 4-2-2 of Gooch. Obviously, for the very elderly *North Star* of 1837, when it was dismantled, certain people in the works arranged for a great many components to be diverted from the scrap yard to 'storage' in selected areas. When the resurrection was ordered in 1924, for display at the British Empire

'King' class 4-6-0 No. 6003 *King George IV* on the down Cornish Riviera Limited, near Reading West, in the late 1930s.   *J. Scott-Morgan Collection*

'King' class No. 6023 *King Edward II*, in somewhat grimy condition with a motley collection of stock, forges up Dainton Bank *c*.1946.   *J. Scott-Morgan Collection*

Exhibition at Wembley the following year, a large number of items, particularly the wheels and motion parts, appeared out of nowhere, to be incorporated in the historic replica.

Whilst the *King George V* and *North Star* were in transit across the Atlantic, having set sail from Cardiff on the SS *Chicago City* on 2nd August, 1927, there was an incident involving No. 6003 *King George IV* which was partially derailed at Midgham when hauling the 'Cornish Riviera Express'. Stanier was, by now, on his way to the USA, and Collett immediately started investigations as to the cause of the derailment which fortunately was confined to the leading bogie only.

The problem was found to be in the springing of the bogie front axle and, after analysis, a redesign ordered. As this redesign proceeded Collett cabled Stanier, ordering that No. 6000 was under no circumstances to be run on the Baltimore and Ohio main line until clearance was received from Swindon, and to organise some workshop space for modifications. By the time the engine had been reassembled, details of the modified springing had reached Stanier, who arranged with the B&ORR for the necessary work to be carried out in their shops under his supervision.

The *King George V* and *North Star* had arrived in the United States on 21st August. After docking and unloading they were conveyed from the quayside at Locust Point to the Mount Clare shops of the Baltimore and Ohio RR in Baltimore. Here the Swindon team was given every assistance to reassemble the locomotives in readiness for the Exhibition. The staff at the Mount Clare shops were very interested in the constructional details and were heard to remark: 'It is not a locomotive, but an automobile.'

On 25th September the Exhibition opened, and more than 1¼ million people were to visit it before the closure on 15th October. *King George V* was accorded the honour of leading the cavalcade of big engines, being given a great reception on each occasion, with the impact of its coasting silently past the crowds, compared to the groaning and clanking of the American engines, arousing much interest in Swindon technology and work standards. One feature of note was the absence of smoke from the GWR engine, both when standing and running on the track.

A great many railroad officers visited the Exhibition and greatly admired the simplicity and workmanship of the engine. Among the many visitors to the 'King' was Mr Henry Ford, who, after the pageant was given a short trip on the footplate. He commented on the smoothness of the working, being particularly interested when he heard it was four-cylindered.

After the close of the Exhibition, arrangements were made to run the locomotive, attached to a special train, between Washington and Philadelphia. A dynamometer car was provided by the B&ORR to head the 6-car train which, in total, weighed 544 tons. For the distance involved of 272 miles this was a formidable load indeed. The coal provided differed from the soft Welsh steam coal used by the GWR and was prone to form large lumps of clinker. This presented some problems for fireman Pearce and it proved difficult to maintain full pressure for long periods of time. However, there was a speed limit of 65 mph imposed so demands for steam were not such as to result in excessive pressure drops beyond that experienced, thanks to the skilful handling of driver Young.

Two views of *King George V* in Canada the USA.

GWR Magazine

Both the Pennsylvania and Hudson Railroads had sent observers to ride on the train who were very impressed by the performance on this demanding run with a maximum load. William, of course, was in the cab with the crew.

William was on hand much of the time to tackle the technical questions and had a good time showing off his new engine. He made a range of new friends and was astonished at the exuberant reception accorded them. There were a few minor crises and Stanier decribed these without drama in his Chairman's address to the Western Branch of the I.Mech.E. following his return to England.

Whilst the 'King' class and other developments had been taking place, Collett had been experimenting with a modified 'Saint' which, in 1924, he had fitted with 6 ft diameter wheels in place of the standard 6 ft 8 in. The Traffic Department was calling for a 4-6-0 variant of the 2-6-0 for mixed traffic duties, and this was a logical answer. It also equated to the missing standard type as specified by Churchward in his list of 1902.

Nearly four years passed before an initial production order was placed, for no fewer than 80. The 'Hall', as it was to become known, proved an immensely successful engine and was to remain in production until 1943. Stanier took note of the versatility of this design and it was to greatly influence his approach to LMS mixed-traffic needs in later years, in the form of the ubiquitous 'Black Five'.

Following his return from the successful USA trip, aged 52, Stanier could not help realizing that he was probably too close to Collett's age of 57 to be a likely candidate for CME of the Great Western; but he had no consuming ambition, enjoyed a high prestige as other Principal Assistants did with their CME, and had a job with a vast store of interest. The 'Hall' class launch was going well and he was engaged in preliminary negotiations with the North British Locomotive Co. for a production batch of fifty '5700' class 0-6-0 pannier tanks in 1929. Moreover the successes of the Great Western were so well publicised that everyone on the line, and especially those around the top, got great job satisfaction, and were already looking forward to their 1935 Centenary celebrations.

In May 1929 a large party of railway officials from France toured the UK and one of their many visits on their list involved Swindon. Collett was unable to receive them, this task being delegated to Stanier who escorted them through the works.

His sporting interests still very much to the fore, William announced in early 1930 that a new sports ground for railway staff would be ready for use in a short while. Encompassing some 13 acres this new facility was on the east side of Swindon south of Shrivenham Road. The land for this had been purchased in August 1928 with funds accrued through the years of Churchward's CME status for, as CME, he was permitted 12 pupils whose fees were traditionally paid to himself. A bachelor, with house provided by the company, and a generous salary, meant that this extra income was to all intents and purposes, surplus to his normal requirements. Also, the premium apprenticeship scheme, when implemented, meant that their fees also came to him. However, Churchward never took any of these monies, having them paid into a holding fund at Paddington. Quite a sizeable sum accrued over the years and, a few

Swindon 'A' shop 1931/2. The locomotive on the crane is No. 5011 *Tintagel Castle*. The 4-6-0 frame in the foreground shows how sparse Churchward made his front frames such that the cylinder/steam chest/smokebox saddle casting could be made in two halves.

W.M. Stanier

'Hall' class 4-6-0 No. 5943 on Weymouth express leaving Bincombe tunnel, south of Dorchester in the late 1930s.   *J. Scott-Morgan Collection*

years after retirement he called Stanier over to 'Newburn' and gave him authority to withdraw the funds to purchase the land. The transaction completed, he handed the land to the GWR on the strict understanding that it was to be used as a sports ground for the benefit of all railway employees.

Collett, by now, could not be persuaded to be involved in anything connected with the social or recreational events in or around Swindon, preferring to delegate all these to William, whose affable approach made him popular as a top management representative.

On the technical side William further widened his arena when he was elected to the Council of the I.Mech.E. and served on the Benevolent Fund and the Engineers Guild and several committees, He quickly established himself as a leading voice on the Membership Committee, becoming its Chairman in 1925 for a six-year spell. His remarkable memory and extraordinarily wide knowledge of people often emerged in brief but authoritative comments; once he unexpectedly vetoed a candidate without explanation, which greatly intrigued the Institution staff, who later found that the reason was an unsavoury brush with the law. ('How on earth did he know?')

On Christmas Eve 1930 the theatre stage portion of the Mechanics Institute at Swindon was destroyed by fire and considerable smoke and water damage ensued. Stanier sprang into energetic action and organised the necessary steps to make good this loss. Opportunity was taken to improve the facilities there. However, by the time the renovated building was opened by the Mayor, on 3rd September, 1932, Stanier had left for his CME position on the LMS. The remainder of this narrative will cover the events from that decisive move.

Stanier as Principal Assistant.   *W.M. Stanier*

Chapter Five

The Transition to the LMS

By 1931, the locomotive position on the LMS was far from satisfactory. Flooded with small engines, much recourse to double-heading was needed to cope with many of the principal expresses. Sir Henry Fowler's 'Royal Scot' class, of which there were 70 in service, was proving to be a reliable locomotive capable of dealing with train weights of 430 tons unaided, but there was a reticence to capitalise on this basically sound design. Sir Henry Fowler had been moved to Research at the end of 1930 and E.J.H. Lemon was now CME, but in a purely holding capacity, whilst Sir Harold Hartley, with the backing of President Sir Josiah Stamp, cast around for a new CME. The trouble with selecting anyone from the many undoubtedly capable engineers within the LMS was the still prevalent partisan outlook, with ex-London & North Western Railway (LNWR), ex-Midland Railway (MR) and ex-Lancashire & Yorkshire Railway (L&YR) personnel plugging their own individual lines.

Hartley was new to the railway scene, a Fellow of the Royal Society and Fellow and Tutor of Balliol College, Oxford, he brought an independent mind to his position of Vice-President and Director of Scientific Research. One of the first questions he asked of the CME's department, which came under his remit, concerned the double-heading from Euston and St Pancras of trains normally employing a single locomotive on the other railways. He was, to put it mildly, not impressed with the answers he got.

The LMS Board agreed with Hartley's assessment of the need to head up the CME's department with a new broom and left it for him to search for a suitable person.

During his 30 years at Oxford, Hartley mentioned in a communication to H.A.V. Bulleid, he had learnt about the Churchward tradition, he also liked the Great Western performance from his journeys to and from Oxford and he therefore decided that Stanier was the best man for the job. This analysis was communicated to Lemon and Fowler who had no difficulty in corroborating it.

October 1931 found William Stanier lunching at the Athenaeum with Hartley, ostensibly to discuss water softening and its effect on boiler maintenance. William was, initially, a bit puzzled at this approach but duly communicated news of it to Collett at Swindon. Shortly after this a further lunch invitation arrived from Hartley, this time at the Traveller's Club. Collett gave the go-ahead and sure enough, at this venue came the question - would Stanier be prepared to take over as CME of the LMS? Tactfully, William suggested that Sir Josiah Stamp and Sir James Milne, respectively the President of the LMS and General Manager of the GWR, should be formally notified of this offer. A further meeting with Stamp then closed the deal after stating his (Stamp's) concern at the large number of locomotive classes on the LMS and emphasising the need for a standard range of larger, more powerful, engines.

By now, William's involvement in both GWR and the Swindon community was burgeoning. With Collett steadfastly refusing to get involved with much outside of the CME's responsibilities, and very selective in what he covered in the social side of railway affairs, much was devolved onto his principal assistant.

A Fowler 'Royal Scot' No. 6155 *The Lancer* on a North Wales express leaving Chester, c.1931/2.

So far as local organisations were concerned William was a founder member of Swindon Rotary Club, being elected as President in 1929; he also chaired the 'Toc H' House Committee, was a Governor of Swindon Secondary School, a Director of both the Swindon Gas Company and Swindon Permanent Building Society, in addition to being President of the Swindon Rugby and Athletic Clubs. To crown all these local positions he was also elected as a JP in early 1931.

One organisation very close to his heart was the Swindon Boy's Red Triangle Club. He had given it his time, thought and influence over many years and for some time had been both Chairman and President. A special service was held just before William's departure at which he was presented with a copy of Lord Birkenhead's 'Collection of English Essays' as a token of appreciation for all he had done for past and present members of the club. In his speech of thanks he emphasised the need to keep a balance between work and play, stating: 'Until a man has acquired that habit, he has not really started to live.'

So far as the GWR affairs went, Presidencies of the GWR Medical Fund Society, GWR Mechanics Institution, GWR Locomotive and Carriage Department Sick and Benefit Society and the GWR Sports Club came his way. On top of these he had also been the Chairman of the GWR Social and Educational Union.

All the above organisations were very saddened when he announced his impending move to the LMS. He had served their causes faithfully and diligently over the years, becoming a highly respected local figure the loss of whom would be difficult to replace. There were several farewell gatherings at which their thanks were proffered. Two of these farewells were reported in the local press, the first being the Rotary Club farewell luncheon at which the presentation of a case of pipes was made by the President, Mr G.H. Burkhardt. Also reported was the GWR Social and Educational Union's fifth annual exhibition of arts and crafts held at the Baths, Swindon, in December 1931. Nelle attended this as usual to distribute the awards, this year being presented with a spectacular bouquet by a Master Alan Peck* at the conclusion of this final social gathering.

William had spent all his life in and around Swindon, so the break from his home town was quite a wrench, and the new task on the LMS was a challenge to which he was to rise spectacularly, a challenge which would alter the motive power story on that railway and raise it to a level equal to, if not better than, the best in the UK. As he himself said to a local reporter just before he departed: 'Swindon will go on, and for me will always hold fond and happy memories.'

Stanier was now 56, with a wealth of experience behind him, and his new position commenced on 1st January, 1932. A position with an awesome responsibility, that of providing a new range of top-class modern locomotives, the production of which also included the task of introducing new manufacturing techniques in the works and, decidedly trickier, of reshaping the CME's department into a coherent entity with its drawing offices all facing, so to speak, in the same direction. It was said that Stanier lacked political acumen but this was just an exaggeration; he just could not imagine anyone actually suppressing or distorting facts to make a political point. Equally, he took time to grasp the extent and implications of the rivalry between Crewe, Derby and Horwich works, and between three drawing offices.

He took office purposefully, arriving at Euston with a large box of GWR drawings which Collett had permitted him to take for reference. Lemon thankfully

* Later to become the works' biographer - *The Great Western at Swindon Works*, published by the Oxford Publishing Co., 1983.

The 0-4-4T, really a Fowler design. These useful but dated little locomotives were mainly used for light branch passenger work. No. 6048 is found on such a duty with a St Albans Abbey train at Watford Junction 4th September, 1937. *J.M. Jarvis*

NCC 2-6-0 No. 97 *Earl of Ulster* at Belfast York Road, 7th August, 1936. *J.M. Jarvis*

handed over the responsibilities of the CME's office to William, making sure that he was at hand to effect the early introductions. It could have been a difficult time for Stanier but his friendly, approachable, manner behind the sheer physical size and penetrating, almost black, eyes soon had his new staff at ease whilst they waited to see how he was going to tackle the monumental task awaiting him.

Shortly after settling in at Euston, William paid his first of many visits to the Derby Locomotive Drawing Office (LDO). Beames, as Deputy CME, conducted him around at a sedate pace, as his gammy leg necessitated a walking stick to support himself. Harold Chambers, the chief draughtsman was there to cover the technical queries and effect any introductions, should they be needed.

One of the current projects was an 0-4-4T, which was a throw-back to the last days of Fowler and had been authorised by Lemon. William pored over the diagram with Chambers, who appeared to some of the staff to be on tenterhooks with this first enquiring visit by the new CME. Some discussion over the valves ensued with Stanier pressing for long travel. It was diplomatically pointed out that this design followed its Johnson derivative with the original slide valves, space for piston valves being impossible without a major redesign of the front end. Long travel was out of the question. This design, the last locomotive to have been started under Fowler, was an update of a Johnson 0-4-4T. Just prior to Fowler's move to research, the drawings had been completed by the Derby LDO and submitted for approval of an initial production batch of ten. Somehow, in E.J.H. Lemon's year as CME this rather antiquated proposal was approved and construction was under way at Derby when Stanier took office. He saw no reason to cancel this programme as the materials were bought and allocated, so the 10 tanks duly appeared and were distributed for use on light branch passenger and freight work.

Another design coming along at this time was a 2-6-0 for the Northern Counties Committee (NCC). Stanier wisely left this to the LDO once he realised that this locomotive was basically a tender version of the Fowler 2-6-4T, which did have long travel valves. He did suggest top feed to the boiler, having a set of Swindon drawings sent up for the draughtsman to use as a guide, plus suggesting that the cab be styled on that of the new 2-6-0 being schemed up at Horwich. The Derby team followed his suggestions and the resulting engine had a distinctive Stanier flavour with these two features.

Coming in as a very senior man, his stature endorsed by the scale of the job, and with a rather direct manner, not given to making compliments and jokes, to those outside his immediate staff he appeared to be an austere and awe-inspiring figure - much more so than Hughes or Fowler and rather more than E.J.H. Lemon. Yet he was always ready to discuss any problem and to devote time and his full attention to the matter in hand. He liked to ensure that a discussion was completed without the people involved becoming distracted by irrelevant but perhaps more dramatic news. A good example happened in July 1933 when he sent for Riddles from Crewe to be his assistant at Euston. Only after a discussion about No. 6201 *Princess Royal*, did he say, 'Oh, by the way, I want you up here on Tuesday,' adding a sensational footnote, 'the Directors have agreed to double your salary.' His choice of staff was always very shrewd and his brand of leadership was to get the best out of them.

Fowler 2-6-4T No. 2379, a Derby product of 1932, at Watford Junction Shed 10th July, 1937.

J.M. Jarvis

Fowler 'Patriot' 4-6-0 No. 5905 on down express, passing Elstree 1934.

R.S. Carpenter Collection

On further minor, but crucial fact, which may have had some impact on Stanier's acceptance of the LMS offer was that he was only five years younger than Collett and could therefore hope for a five-year term as CME if Collett retired at 65. However, some time prior to the move, Collett had casually mentioned that he intended going on to the age of 70, as 'the Chairman has asked me to do that.' A brief sojourn at age 65 was not attractive to Stanier, even if he was fit and capable. There were several up-and-coming younger men at Swindon just as able.

One of the first major decisions awaiting him was the matter of a batch of Fowler 'Patriot' 4-6-0s on order. As many components had been manufactured and with most of the material in stock he permitted their construction, subject to them being modified to accept changes to the bogies and axleboxes. His decision was based on the excellent performance being shown by the two prototypes and a further 50 were to be authorised to assist the 70 'Royal Scots' available.

Stanier made sure he was available for the early 1932 Locomotive Committee meetings and presented a case for a new express locomotive to bolster the 'Scots' and 'Patriots'. What he proposed was a larger design than either of these two, a Pacific being at the back of his mind as a logical layout to permit long non-stop runs of around 400 miles as was the Euston-Glasgow turn, which at present involved an engine change at Carlisle. Schedules could be speeded up on that premier route and he was accorded funds to go ahead with three examples in July 1932.

It was, in fact, 29th April, 1932 when some of the first line diagrams for Stanier's proposed new standard locomotives arrived at the Derby LDO. These were a Pacific and a rebuilt 'Claughton', both with taper boilers. The former was to become the 'Princess Royal' class and the latter the 'Jubilee' 4-6-0. Taper boilers were not unknown in the Derby drawing office, for as far back as 1908, Deeley had designed a 4-cylinder compound 4-6-0 which employed a boiler tapered on the back ring together with a tapered Belpaire firebox, rather reminiscent of the early Churchward variants. The final shape was very similar to Swindon practice, but this design was effectively squashed by the Midland Railway small engine policy. Contrary to some belief, Swindon boiler drawings were not supplied to the LDO and the draughtsmen actually used to guide them a July 1919 issue of the *Railway Engineer* which had an article and details of GW boilers.

Based on his line diagrams, William ordered some studies to be made taking the earlier Fowler compound Pacific as a starting point, but employing simple expansion. The early schemes for this had three cylinders, with the motion based on that of the 'Scots', but this was quickly changed to the four-cylinder format based on the GWR 'King' class. He was not going to be dictated to by the traditionalists still plugging the LMS three-cylinder layouts for what was to become a radical new express type.

H.P.M. Beames, the Deputy Chief Mechanical Engineer, based at Derby, had taken Stanier's appointment stoicly, as by normal railway standards he should have been given the job and immediately registered his support in a thoughtful welcoming note, which included the following comment: '. . . but I may say that there is no one I would rather work under than you'.

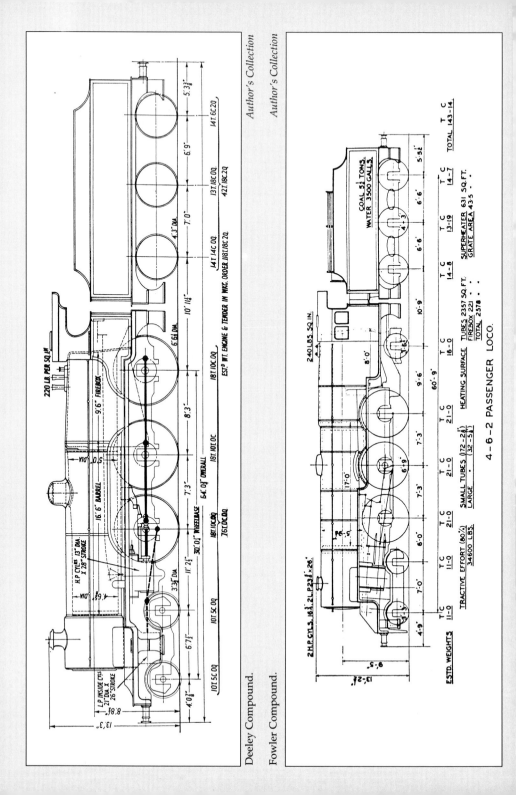

Deeley Compound.

Fowler Compound.

Chapter Six

Settling at Euston

William was finding the production set-up on the LMS totally different to the GWR, there were four major large works compared to the one at Swindon. Additionally, the running side was not responsible to the CME as it had been on the GWR, but came under a Chief Motive Power Superintendent, James Anderson. Stanier and Anderson took to each other from the start, but sometimes did not see eye to eye. Anderson would specify so many engines of an existing type when asked for future needs, and the memorandum containing the request was put in Stanier's 'pending' tray. When asked why no reply was forthcoming, William replied firmly: 'I am trying to decide what new locomotives are needed, and can only do this if you will specify the numbers and the duties they are to perform.' Anderson got the message and co-operated over the remaining time of his service, for he retired in late 1932, to be replaced by another Scot, D.C.Urie, formerly the Divisional Mechanical Engineer, Scotland.

Urie was the son of R.W. Urie, the former CME of the London & South Western Railway, who had retired at Grouping. Stanier replaced Urie with H.G. Ivatt, who was Works Superintendent at Derby, and had instigated the efficient shopping system for locomotive repairs at that plant whilst under Fowler.

The initial response to Stanier's appointment by the design staff at Derby was that the drawing office had made a point of assiduously studying GWR locomotive practice immediately it became known that he was to be the new CME. This was in order that they might be able (so they thought) to communicate better with him. In fact the communication, when it came, was direct and forthright as William began to make inroads into the 'Midland' philosophy. In his own words: 'The first year it was difficult to get the Drawing Office to change from Midland practice to what I wanted to carry out. But after that I had no trouble at all.'

Churchward had always been a great believer in large bearing surfaces, his standard engines had large journals and the bearings were so designed that they had a running clearance on each side to build up the oil film with a proper wool and horsehair pad to keep the journal flooded with oil. As a result his engines were remarkably free from hot boxes. Stanier took this precept with himself to the LMS, no more were new locomotives to be plagued with the inadequate '4F' box promoted for so many years by Derby drawing office. This adverse feature had only been avoided on the 'Royal Scot', the 2-6-4T and the 'Crab' 2-6-0, the 'Scot' by being designed under contract by the North British Locomotive Company and the other two, which had common frame and chassis features, had essentially been Horwich designs of Hughes.

Although one of the success stories on the GWR had been the introduction of the semi-plug piston valve, Stanier decided that it was not feasible to introduce this on the LMS. He had, we have seen, experienced the troubles in getting these valves properly installed at Swindon and, bearing in mind he had four main

The Hughes 2-6-0 No. 13110 rests between duties at what may be Crewe Shed.
R.S. Carpenter Collection

Hughes 2-6-0 No. 13096 found at Sheffield Grimesthorpe Shed 1927.   *R.S. Carpenter Collection*

works on the LMS to educate in the specialised techniques in their machine shops, decided not to introduce this feature. What finally tipped the balance in this decision was the fact that by this time the four simple narrow rings in the piston valve head employed by the LMS gave quite good results. Stanier ordered that these should be narrowed slightly and a total of six installed instead on all future designs. The expense of switching to something which gave only a marginal improvement could not be justified.

On the works side, Stanier found much to impress him. The Crewe boiler-making standards were of Swindon quality but cheaper. Even though they were rather small for the duties they performed and were thrashed to produce the steam needed, they did not need excessive maintenance and lasted well. Despite this positive finding he determined to continue the introduction of Swindon-style taper boilers with their better circulation and steaming properties. However, in connection with the quality of work at Crewe and Derby some diplomacy certainly worked wonders where some obvious dislike of changes in working practices were concerned. As Stanier said much later when discussing his early days on the LMS: 'I had to suggest to the people at Crewe and Derby that they were quite as good as Swindon. After this I had no trouble.'

In 1932, as he began to assert his authority, Stanier was responsible for what some would now class as heresy in dealing with some rather historic relics brought to his attention. In similar vein to Churchward's earlier edict to scrap the two remaining broad gauge locomotives at Swindon, the 4-2-2 *Lord of the Isles* and the even earlier 2-2-2 *North Star*, William, on finding the Derby paint shop cluttered up with a clutch of preserved locomotives, ordered their scrapping. 'Preserved engines? I haven't authorised any engines to be preserved. Scrap them', he is reported as having said. Someone clearly had the temerity to stand up to this edict, but only managed to save the Johnson 4-2-2 for posterity. The others - a Kirtley 2-4-0 and 0-6-0, Johnson 0-4-0T and ex-North London 4-4-0T, were consigned to the cutter's torch. He had a just case, in that they were taking up valuable space, but the loss of these historic MR and NLR locomotives was particularly sad, when we look back from an era in which preservation is very much the way to keep alive the steam past.

The new Pacific was being designed whilst all this settling in took place and only 17 months after Stanier arrived on the LMS the first of two prototypes, No. 6200 *The Princess Royal,* was turned out by Crewe.

Here at last was a thoroughly modern express type, using much of the details laid down by Fowler's abortive compound Pacific exercise, which itself was derived from a Hughes L&YR design study of late pre-Grouping days. Stanier, however, had insisted on the incorporation of a number of Swindon features, a domeless taper boiler and low degree superheat being the major ones. Valve gear was Walschaerts with long travel and long lap, four independent sets being provided, this being a break from the Swindon practice of two sets and rocking shafts. Due to the pressure of time the drawing office had not managed to work out a satisfactory system of lever operation for two sets of gear. As Stanier said himself later: 'It wasn't until I had Coleman as chief draughtsman that I had what I wanted in that direction'.

'Princess Royal' class No. 6200, as yet un-named, in Crewe works yard.   *J. Alsop Collection*

Stanier's 'Jubilee' as built, No. 5649 at Bedford Shed on 18th April, 1936.   *J.M. Jarvis*

One further break from Swindon tradition was the provision of a wide firebox which was needed to provide adequate grate area for the different quality of fuel prevalent on the LMS. (The GWR still relied on Welsh steam coal more to the liking of their narrow fireboxes.) In addition a long 6 to 7 hour run as envisaged for the West Coast Main line would result in the ashpan of a narrow firebox becoming choked with the products of combustion towards the end, with drastic consequences on steaming ability. The leading bogie followed the Churchward/de Glehn form so successfully adopted by the GWR and materially contributed to the riding qualities of the Pacifics.

This new locomotive was largely the work of the Derby drawing office, and as he began to assess the capabilities of the three main design teams available to him, Stanier placed a directive on the Horwich team to design a new mixed-traffic 2-6-0 to augment the Hughes 'Crab', that class then totalling some 225 examples. This drawing office was chosen by Stanier because he was not overly impressed with the leading figures in the Crewe DO, which was backing up the effort at Derby, this latter office involved in scheming a 3-cylinder 4-6-0 to supplement the 'Royal Scot' and 'Patriot' fleets. As the designs of the 2-6-0 and 4-6-0 proceeded, it was decided to make the 2-6-0 boiler a shortened version of that being developed for the 4-6-0. It simplified Crewe's work on boiler construction and was a straight copy of what had been done much earlier at Swindon. One criticism of the taper boilers was that they were expensive to make, requiring extra tooling for jointing the rings, so anything which would reduce costs, such as this commonality, was welcome.

T.F. Coleman, at Horwich, gathered together a good team of contract draughtsmen and soon had the 2-6-0 schemed. William, on his visits to Horwich, recognised in Coleman a competent designer and leader who did not baulk at new ideas, was confident in his fast-working team, and made a mental note to make some adjustments to the design hierarchy when circumstances were appropriate. So it was not surprising that as the Pacifics took the rails, the 2-6-0 was not far behind. The 3-cylinder 4-6-0 was to take much longer.

Stanier could have taken the easy way out and ordered more examples of the Hughes design, but saw the opportunity to introduce Swindon ideas to the Horwich team. He saw no reason to retain the rather ungainly high-mounted cylinders, as he was to introduce the GWR 225 psi tapered boiler developed all those years ago by Churchward. Hughes, had steadfastly refused to condone a boiler pressure of more than 180 psi which, to achieve the tractive effort desired, had meant employing large diameter cylinders. These needed to be placed high to avoid fouling the loading gauge, whereas Stanier's 2-6-0 had cylinders 3 inches less in diameter and could be mounted horizontally looking aesthetically more pleasing. The LMS Civil Engineer's Department claimed that some 300 platforms would be fouled, even going so far as providing a list of the suspect sites. However, Stanier wondered how much this actually applied and sent some 'Crabs' fitted with lead feelers appropriate to the outline of both the new 2-6-0 with its horizontal cylinders and the new Pacific round the 300 locations listed as being potential restrictions. Only a few were found to be so, and these were easily altered by resetting the platform edge stones.

Above: Royal Scot as fitted out for the American tour.   *I.Mech.E.*

Right and below: Royal Scot's arrival at Euston on return from USA.
                                        W.M. Stanier

An initial batch of 10 2-6-0s was authorised in 1932, being built at Crewe in 1933. Unknown to Stanier, the drawing office at Horwich, in an effort to please their new CME, placed a typical GWR safety valve casing on the production drawings and the first example appeared with this on 21st October, 1933. Stanier, however, was not at all pleased and ordered its immediate removal. 'We are not here to produce carbon copies of Swindon practice', he is said to have exclaimed angrily. This first batch also had the safety valves on the boiler barrel but on all future members of this class, which eventually totalled 40, these reverted to the more conventional firebox position. The original 10 were modified to this as they came in for major overhaul.

At Swindon, Churchward had set up an Experimental Section in the drawing office, which dealt with all schemes for improvements in locomotive design and also any project studies. Stanier, once settled in at Euston, ordered that a similar section be created within the Derby drawing office, putting S.J. Symes in charge. However, it did not perform as well as he hoped, as in his own words: 'But I did not get as much from it as what I hoped - too Midland.' Symes had been a leading figure in the DO under Fowler in MR days and was steeped in the ways commonplace to that railway, so it was not surprising matters stagnated somewhat.

As 1933 approached the LMS received an invitation to send a locomotive and train to the USA to be exhibited at the Chicago 'Century of Progress' exhibition. Much as Stanier would have liked to send one of the new Pacifics, there simply was not enough time to bring forward the completion to meet the deadline. Therefore Stanier ordered that No. 6152 of the 'Royal Scot' class be completely refurbished at Derby with new axleboxes to his specification and a new bogie based on the GWR/de Glehn type commonplace at Swindon. He also revised the springing of the driving wheels as he was of the opinion that the engine did not ride too well. The small Fowler tender was replaced with one intended for Pacific No. 6202 and the engine swapped its name and number with No. 6100.

In March 1933, just before the locomotive and train were to be shipped over, the financial crisis in the American banks came to a head, with President Roosevelt issuing an edict closing every bank in the country. But, in an effort to keep a grasp on normality, the tour planned for the *Royal Scot* in North America went ahead unchecked.

Following an initial tour of nearly 2,632 miles through the Eastern parts of Canada and the United States, the train was put on display at Chicago, after which it embarked on an 8,562 mile tour of the USA and Canada upon which it displayed excellent reliability. Thousands of people crowded onto the train to inspect the carriages during its many stops on the lengthy journey. The American railroads over which the train travelled had stationed pilot engines along the route as, when they saw the size of the locomotive compared to their own massive stock, they had found it difficult to believe that it could cope over some of the gradients to be encountered. For example there was a steep gradient between Chicago and Cincinnati which, driver Gilbertson was warned, would tax the locomotive somewhat. In the course of that run, Gilbertson asked of his American pilotman: 'When are we coming to that hill?' The reply was: 'You're over it.'

Stanier 2-6-0 No. 13247 at Crewe in almost brand-new condition.

R.S. Carpenter Collection

Upon completion of the tour at Windsor station, Montreal, the locomotive and train were taken to the Angus Shops of the Canadian National Railway for preparation before being loaded onto the SS *Beaverdale* for the voyage home, which was slightly delayed when the vessel ran aground in the St Lawrence shortly after setting sail. After arrival back in England, the train was re-railed and the locomotive serviced ready for a publicity run down to Euston. On 15th December, the *Royal Scot* glided slowly into Euston, with the brightly polished bell provided for its North American journeying clanging. The station was specially decorated for the occasion and the pipe band of the LMS 21st Scouts and Rovers played the wanderer home. Sir Josiah Stamp, at the short ceremony that followed, then presented commemorative gold watches to the team that had accompanied the train on its historic journey.

One feature of William's expertise, that of machine tools, was used early on in his time as CME, in that he asked for, and obtained, sanction for improved modern machines to re-equip the works. During the early works tours his keen eyes had noticed the antiquity of some equipment still in use. He also introduced the pleasing GWR ritual of making cast bronze replicas of new engines, nicely painted in the correct colours by the paint shop. He had a boiler shop trick that impressed H.G. Ivatt and positively paralysed one of the boiler inspectors - a method of sliding his considerable frame through a firehole door without soiling his clothes. And he had a neat trick in letter-signing; his clerk applied a facsimile of 'W.A.S.' and, if he approved of the letter, he merely added 'tanier' [this was common practice on the GWR].

He had settled in well and speedily, he needed to, for there was a pressing need for more express locomotives, and the Design Offices at Derby and Horwich were coming along with several schemes for consideration. This time the main thrust was to be for the Pacific, the story of the development of which is covered in detail in the next Chapter.

Stanier 2-6-0 No. 13267 at Crewe Shed 1935. *R.S. Carpenter Collection*

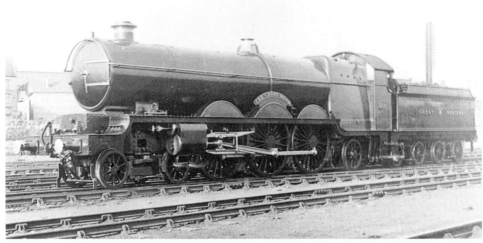

The single Churchward Pacific *The Great Bear* 4-6-2 on shed at Old Oak Common 1912.
R.S. Carpenter Collection

The frames of No. 6200 being erected at Crewe in 1933.   *R.S. Carpenter Collection*

Chapter Seven

The Pacifics

In his early days on the LMS, William had frequently visited Churchward at 'Newburn' in Swindon for consultations. One of the problems he must have discussed was the need for a really powerful express type capable of covering the 400 miles between Euston and Glasgow non-stop. It has been speculated that Churchward, mindful of the potential behind his now defunct *The Great Bear*, suggested that a Pacific was the logical answer, and said he should take the 'King' as a baseline to use for a starting point. Stanier had taken a set of 'King' drawings to the LMS and it was perfectly in order to develop a Pacific from the 'King', as Churchward had taken the 'Star' 4-6-0 to develop his *Great Bear* 4-6-2.

However, these meetings were suddenly curtailed after the dreadful tragedy of December 1933, when Churchward was killed by a South Wales express while he was inspecting the track adjoining the garden of 'Newburn'. This event shook the whole railway engineering world. Stanier was one of the many CMEs, past and present, who attended the funeral in Swindon of that great engineer. The ARLE meeting following this tragic loss was significant in that all those present stood in silence as a mark of respect to their old colleague of former years. Collett was present, but this was to be the last peacetime meeting he attended. His interest in the Association was waning and he was beginning to withdraw more and more into himself, still grieving over his 1923 loss of his wife. At this meeting Stanier proposed R.A. Riddles, now his Principal Assistant on locomotive matters, for membership.

As regards sheer size and performance, the Stanier Pacifics were to raise the LMS to the forefront of express locomotive developments in the UK. The first two, Nos. 6200 and 6201, were very much allied to Swindon technology with domeless taper boiler, top feed and low degree superheat. However, we have seen that Stanier did break away from some Swindon practices, particularly for the valve gear. The front of the engine was very similar to the GWR 'King' 4-6-0 and the substantial rear end with a wide Belpaire firebox gave a balanced look over the length of the engine. The tractive effort was, as for the GWR 'King', 40,300 lb.

The prototype was to be somewhat of a hybrid at the end of the design study to specify it. Apart from the details mentioned above, the motion for the inside cylinders was typically GW as in the 'Kings', the rear pony truck had been taken from the abortive Fowler compound Pacific schemes, and the cab styling was typical Horwich handed down via the Hughes 4-6-2 which had been adopted by Fowler on his Pacific. With all these different sources for components it proved difficult for Chambers to come to grips with the weight estimates. He could see that the engine was going to come out very heavy, as although it was estimated to weigh 103 tons the first weighing after construction for No. 6200 came out at 111 tons. Some remedial work by the LDO in providing lightening holes and thinner castings resulted a value of 104 tons for No. 6201, which became the standard for this class.

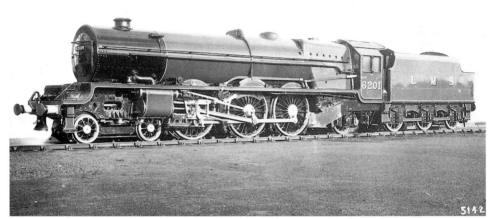

Stanier Pacific No. 6201 *Princess Elizabeth*.   *J. Alsop Collection*

Pacific No. 6203 *Princess Margaret Rose* is seen at Crewe.   *J. Alsop Collection*

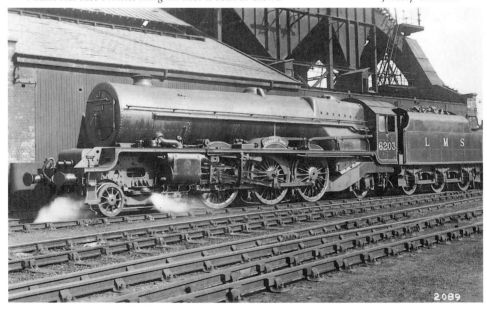

Chambers was considerably relieved at the outcome of the weight reduction exercise. A worrying sort like him tended to take problems very much to heart, and this was to be a feature leading to a breakdown in health, illness and a relatively early death.

The inspection by Stanier, at Crewe works, of the prototype Pacific when completed in May 1933, resulted in a slight contratemps as regards its finish. Several patches of rust were evident as well as some castings left as received from the Foundry. William commented on the Crewe lack of finesse, asking could they not turn out a locomotive to Swindon standards. The point was taken, and two weeks later the engine, now looking like a new product, was driven to Euston for inspection by the Board. Nelle was there and dutifully walked down the platform to examine her husband's handiwork. She remarked on the lack of a name at that time, being partially mollified by the driver's comment: 'Well, we call it the Baby Austin.'

The initial trials produced some indication of poor steaming and initially No. 6201 was fitted with a double chimney and double blastpipe nozzles, the front one taking the exhaust from the inside cylinders and the rear from the outside cylinders. This was totally ineffective, only producing worse steaming and was speedily changed back to a single blastpipe and chimney. With evidence of poor performance of the low degree superheating coming from other designs emerging in 1934/5, Stanier finally realised that Swindon ideas on superheating were not amenable to the LMS scene. Accordingly No. 6200 was fitted with a new boiler employing a 32 element superheater in April 1935 - and the performance was transformed.

By now Stanier had had the design team prepare the drawings for a new tender to replace the high flat-sided version supplied initially. The new tender had high curved sides blending in with the cab roof profile and held 4,000 gallons of water and 9 tons of coal. The production batch of 10 appeared with these from new.

The 'Princess Royal' Pacifics, as they were known, were, it appears, just as speedy as their later streamlined cousins, for on 3rd May, 1936, No. 6203 was rostered for a test train to carry out some trials on braking from high speed ordered by Stanier. The Dynamometer car plus a six coach set made a total train weight of 208 tons. Some of the coaches had floor panels removed for visual observation of the braking action on the bogies. The test was from Crewe to Willesden and return. On one of the runs a speed of 104 mph was reported, although this value is contradicted by the one of 102 mph mentioned in the *LMS Magazine* report of this trial. Speed was set at 90 mph by milepost 23 south of Boxmoor and the brakes fully applied. The train took 63 seconds to come to a complete halt. Stanier, who rode in the Dynamometer car, had observers placed in the coaches to give an account of how the braking affected the stock.

The development of the further Pacifics, which were built through to 1948, is a tale of progressive development, including two particular unique variations, the turbine powered version and the introduction of streamlining to the LMS. These will be briefly covered in turn.

As he went through the files in the CME's department, William had noted the reports of the trials of the Beyer-Ljungstrom turbine-powered locomotive by

The frames of the 'Turbomotive' at Crewe on 3rd March, 1935. Note the complex piping for the turbine control units.   *R.S. Carpenter Collection*

The 'Turbomotive', No. 6202.   *I.Mech.E.*

Fowler in 1927. Reports in the technical press and a conversation with Dr H.L. Guy, the Chief Engineer of the Metropolitan Vickers Electrical Co. Ltd, concerning a Swedish turbine powered locomotive aroused his further interest. This Swedish engine was of the non-condensing type, the previous Beyer-Ljungstrom version having had the disadvantage of requiring a complex and weighty condensing tender. Stanier immediately realised that the non-condensing concept could offer a lighter answer to the possibility of turbine power. Dr Guy proposed to visit Sweden to see this new locomotive in action and William decided to accompany him, taking along with himself the chief draughtsman from Derby.

They travelled over in mid-1932 to visit the Grangeberg-Oxelsund Railway and investigate the Ljungstrom non-condensing Turbine locomotive, a 2-8-0 freight type which had been in regular service since May. The eight coupled wheels were driven via a triple reduction gear-box and jackshaft by a 1,200 hp turbine using steam at 185 psi and superheated to 750°F. Reversing was by means of an idler gear in the gear-box. Trains of 1,550 tons of iron ore were hauled up a 1 in 100 gradient, at a recorded drawbar pull of 21.6 tons with consummate ease - an impressive demonstration. Despite being a non-condensing turbine, a reduction in water consumption, compared to an equivalent conventional locomotive, was some 18 per cent, with an equivalent fuel saving of over 9 per cent.

Upon their return to the UK, Stanier and Guy produced a report of their findings and thus began a collaborative exercise between the LMS and Metropolitan Vickers. The third Pacific authorised in 1932 was cancelled in favour of the turbine proposal. The bogie, wheels, pony truck, and frames and many other parts of the experimental locomotive were very similar to the cancelled third example of the 'Princess Royal' class, so tooling was minimal. The turbine equipment contract was placed with Metropolitan Vickers and construction of the chassis commenced at Crewe.

By mid-1934, Metropolitan-Vickers had started manufacture of the power turbines for the experimental locomotive and the Derby LDO was commencing on the boiler final design. This was different to the units fitted to Nos. 6200 and 6201 as these two prototypes had, initially, 16 large tubes for the superheater elements, whereas the turbine version started with 32. This was due to the need to have hot, dry, steam for the turbine. Any risk of saturated steam was to be avoided as this could result in water droplets damaging the turbine blades.

A feature of the new boiler was that a combustion chamber was specified. The Fowler compound Pacific had been designed with one and the drawings were got out to provide a starting point for the draughtsman given the boiler design task, E.A. Langridge. A point of interest surrounding this boiler design was that, when further Pacifics of the 'Princess Royal' class were ordered they employed a similar design having 32 element superheaters, but a slightly different layout of small tubes. One of the prototypes, No. 6201, had been fitted with this design of boiler earlier. This came about because there was a delay with the Metropolitan Vickers equipment, and as this boiler for the turbine locomotive was complete and had sat around unused for some time, it was decided to try out the effect of higher superheat on the first two engines, this

The 'Turbomotive' arrives at Euston after a proving run to be inspected by the 'top brass'.
W.M. Stanier

The 'Turbomotive' awaits departure from Euston on a test train when almost new in 1935.
R.S. Carpenter Collection

boiler being fitted to No. 6201. This change soon showed a considerable improvement in performance and for all future Pacifics high degree superheat was taken as standard.

In June 1935 the turbine locomotive entered traffic and began to show promise. It was much liked by the crews due to the smooth riding characteristics obtained from the turbine power transmission. Some problems occurred, but not sufficient to warrant more than a few days in works. In fact, for 1936, the total miles run were 73,268 which compared well with the average 80,000 miles per locomotive run for the 'Princess Royal' class as a whole.

No. 6202, or the 'Turbomotive' as it became called, was a centre of some interest to Stanier and Guy. They both liked the nickname bestowed on it 'Gracie Fields' (because it sang as it went). The LMS Board winced a bit at the final cost of £20,538 compared to the £8,538 for the other 'Princess Royals', of which a further batch of a 10 was under construction as the turbine prototype took the rails.

The major part of the design exercise for the 'Turbomotive' had been carried out using the Derby drawing office, who arranged the closest co-operation with the turbine manufacturers. The general specification called for the capability of working 500 ton trains between London and Glasgow. This equated to a turbine power output of 2,600 hp with an estimated starting tractive effort of 40,000 lb. and 12,000 lb. sustained at 70 mph, the estimated speed for maximum turbine efficiency.

No 6202 was, aesthetically, an elegant looking locomotive and, on the whole, performed satisfactorily in service, bearing in mind its experimental status. Certainly some failures occurred, but the mileage run in 1936 was creditable for such a machine. Some accounts of the 'Turbomotive' in service are around, and one which has come to light concerns a trip on the footplate in 1936. The train involved was the mid-day Euston-Liverpool express, which on this occasion loaded to 10 coaches (about 310 tons), quite a light load for the locomotive.

When the regulator was opened to start, there was no jerk as would have happened with a standard Pacific, just a smooth, steady, acceleration with absolutely no nosing associated with the reciprocating motion of conventional types. The thrust was steady and straight ahead. Once up to speed the performance of the 'Turbomotive' was much as for the standard Pacific, even when climbing grades. The crews appreciated the smoothness of the locomotive, as it made their task on the footplate much more comfortable. It was also quiet in operation, as the turbine exhaust produced little sound, just a soft hissing noise backed by a slight whine from the turbine itself. The impression was of silent power. Stanier and Guy could well be proud of their creation, development of which was sadly curtailed by World War II. Those who knew Stanier have said that, circumstances permitting, he would have liked to seen a small fleet of 'Turbomotives' built. This would certainly have eased the spares problems which plagued the prototype all its life, plus reducing the unit cost by quantity production. Turbine applications to locomotive technology did not end with the 'Turbomotive', however, as we shall see at the end of Chapter Eleven.

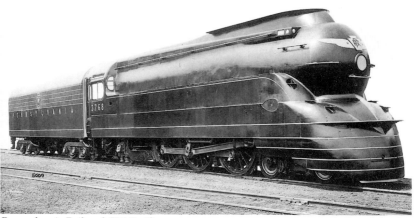

Pennsylvania Railroad 'K4' Pacific.   *J. Alsop Collection*

In 1936, William paid another visit to the USA and spent some time with the Pennsylvania Railroad. At that time plans for speeding up the LMS express schedules were raising queries about wheel flange stresses on the track and Stanier, with some Pennsylvania engineers, was taking measurements while sundry electric trains went by. Then came a train hauled by a 'K4' Pacific which all concerned stopped to admire. 'There you are,' said Stanier, 'nobody cares a damn for your tin boxes.'

With the 'Turbomotive' built and in service, Stanier then turned his mind to further, improved, Pacifics. Streamlining was in vogue, with Gresley's 'A4' entering service on the LNER. The Board of the LMS agreed to a batch of Pacifics employing this feature, which they reckoned would be good for publicity. Streamlining had, in fact, been briefly considered for the final batch of the 'Princess Royal' class, but they were too far advanced in the shops for this scheme to be adopted. Even so, a ⅟₂₄ scale model had been produced in March 1935 for wind tunnel tests at the Derby Research Department. The general appearance of this early attempt was very much like contemporary German practice, with valances covering much of the motion and wheels.

The first ARLE meeting of 1936 took place at the Great Northern Hotel, Kings Cross on the 28th February. Gresley was still President and, after lunch, conducted the members present to the station to witness the arrival of the 'Silver Jubilee', after which they were taken over the engine and train by a clearly very proud Gresley. Stanier and the others were impressed by the locomotive, the first truly streamlined type to appear in the UK, and by the new articulated carriage sets with their distinctive inter-bogie valances down to a few inches above rail level.

A further event which proved the catalyst for Stanier to consider streamlining was the visit of the Institution of Locomotive Engineers to Germany in May 1936. William had joined, or rather been coaxed into, the I.Loco.E. in 1933 and had in 1936 been elected President. So he was duty bound to lead the party of 100 which departed from Harwich on the 22nd May bound for the Hook of Holland. Awaiting them the next morning on arrival in Holland was a Netherlands Railway train to which had been coupled some Reichsbahn

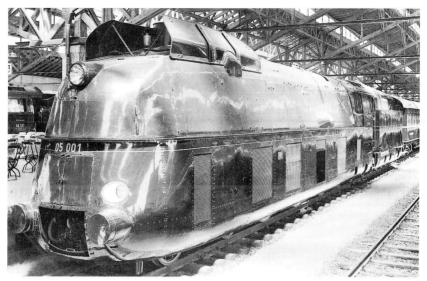

A streamlined German 4-6-4 of class '05'.   *J. Alsop Collection*

coaches and a Mitropa restaurant car. Boarding their coaches they were conveyed to the German border to be met by Dr R.P. Wagner, the chief of the Mechanical Section of the German State Railways.

For the first two days of the tour they were treated to a range of transport mediums, from a steamer on the Rhine to both steam and electric locomotives, on a journey to Munich. Once settled in Munich their first visit to the State Railway facilities was made on the 25th May. Following the works visit, where they saw both steam and electric locomotives undergoing construction and repair, they were given a trip on a special train hauled by a 2-6-2 diesel-hydraulic locomotive. This took them to the M.A.N. works at Augsburg where diesel engines of all sizes were in mass production.

The following three days were spent in and around Bavaria, sampling a wide range of travel modes, from ancient horse-drawn carriages to the latest in railway technology, before finishing up in Nuremburg.

To conclude the tour they were all taken to Berlin where the first visit was to the locomotive testing station at Grunewald, where much interesting work was in progress. Stanier made a mental note to start discussions back home about a similar facility for the LMS.

Hitler had been Chancellor for three years now, and the full might of the Nazi regime was beginning to bite in Germany, even so access to much of the latest in railway developments was open to the Institution members. The evening of the 29th May was taken up with a lavish banquet at the headquarters of the German State Railways, a former Royal Palace, which stood opposite the official residence of Hitler. The latter, much to the relief of the party, was nowhere to be seen.

The tour of German railway works and industry culminated on the 30th with a run to Hamburg and back from Berlin on a special high-speed train hauled by streamlined 4-6-4 No. 05.002. For the first half of the run from the Freidrichstrasse station, Berlin, to Wittenberg, Stanier was invited to ride in the cab of this latest example of German locomotive technology. Much of the 79 miles to Wittenberg was carried out at speeds in excess of 158 km/hr (100 mph), a maximum of 190 km/hr (120 mph) being briefly attained. He was much impressed by the riding of the locomotive, particularly at speeds over 100 mph. It was noticeable that the tour of Germany, although visiting selected industrial and railway centres, pointedly missed out any of the large industries grouped in the Ruhr area. Just over two months previously, German troops had reoccupied the Rhineland, so vital to the defence of these industrial heartlands, in contravention of the Treaty of Versailles. It was through this zone that the special train had sped on its way to the first stop in Cologne.

Once home from the German trip, Stanier reluctantly permitted the streamlining exercise to be applied to the 1937/8 batch of 10 Pacifics that had been authorised and which were to have several changes to the earlier model. Firstly, he had taken note of André Chapelon's insistance on internally streamlining the steam passages and requested this to be followed when scheming out the new engine's front end. Superheating was now high degree, with a 40 element design of 856 sq.ft area, the largest superheating surface of any British locomotive. The boiler was much improved and enlarged, with a tube plus firebox heating surface of 2,807 sq. ft. Coupled wheel diameter was increased to 6 ft 9 in. and the outside valve gear also drove the inside valves via rocker arms, an 'inside-out' version of the standard GWR system.

However, it is worth recording here that Stanier never really wanted to go to the expense of streamlining the new Pacifics. Although wind tunnel tests had resulted in the claim that 400 hp could be saved at speeds in excess of 70 mph, this figure was clearly excessive, as Gresley was only claiming a 65 hp saving at that speed on his 'A4' Pacifics. On the argument that Gresley's number was the more reasonable one (the LNER tests had been conducted at the National Physical Laboratory, so the figures were certainly more believable) and that a fair proportion of the long distance running would not exceed 70 mph, the saving in power required showed only a small reduction in fuel and water consumption. The extra costs incurred in general maintenance due to restricted access under the streamlined carapace would probably have negated that small saving.

William was astute enough to realise this and recommended that the streamlining not be pursued, only to be overruled by a publicity conscious Board.

If the track layout and condition could have permitted long stretches of running at speeds up to 100 mph, only then might streamlining have been worthwhile. Only the GWR had a main line (London to Bristol) which was suitable for such high speeds, but Collett refused to get involved in streamlining other than a half-hearted attempt on two locomotives to placate the GWR Board.

As the detail design work commenced at Derby, Stanier prepared for a three month trip to India with Sir Ralph Wedgwood of the LNER. The reasons for and the description of this trip are given in Chapter Nine. Partly due to this long absence, he was again elected President of the I.Loco.E. in 1937 and at their annual dinner Lord Stamp said: 'It is quite incredible that anybody like Mr Stanier should have survived this date with such a reputation for perfect rectitude as he possesses. His earlier records are, of course, with the Great Western Railway and I cannot get at them. But at any rate he is not loquacious and he has never given himself away'.

In his reply Stanier remarked: 'There are perhaps three types of individuals associated with engineering - the man who can speak, the man who can write, and the man who can do the job. I am conscious of my own failings in expressing myself and I, like the Institution, always encourage young engineers in speaking and writing'.

This second year as President coincided with the appearance of the first batch of streamlined Pacifics, which were intended for the new 'Coronation Scot' special high-speed train being introduced on the Anglo-Scottish service to counter the competitive LNER streamliners then entering their second year of service. The LMS streamliners were a success from the start, steaming and riding excellently. A test run in June 1937 with No. 6220 *Coronation* achieved a maximum speed of 114 mph which caused a minor drama at Crewe as the train thundered in at far too high a speed. 'How foolish to come in so fast' was one typical comment from the waiting officials. 'How foolish to turn a high-speed train into a reverse curve', Stanier retorted, 'merely to bring it alongside a platform', probably quietly reflecting that they would have been derailed but for the Pacific's de Glehn bogie with its excellent control through sharp curves. The next day he sent a personal letter of congratulation to F.A. Lemon, R.C. Bond and co. at Crewe Works; they had produced these larger Pacifics in record time.

Some 24 of the 51 Stanier Pacifics constructed were to be streamlined, although in later years they were eventually rebuilt without the smooth casing - it eased the maintenance at the expense of little measurable degradation in performance or economy.

One notable feature of all the Stanier Pacifics was their capability for high power output over lengthy periods. There are several recorded instances on trials of sustained indicated horsepowers of 2,300- 2,500 on the severe northern climbs *en route* to Carlisle and Glasgow. Even higher values, in excess of a sustained 3,000 ihp have been recorded more recently on the preserved examples over Shap Fell. This latter value called for two firemen such was the coal consumption to produce the steam for this huge effort, which would equate to a steaming rate approaching 40,000 lb./hour. Had mechanical stoking been available, even this rate could have been increased as the boiler was capable of steaming rates well in excess of 40,000 lb./hour.

We need now to go back to 1933 and see how Stanier tackled the other, more mundane but essential, motive power tasks awaiting him after his arrival in the CME's chair.

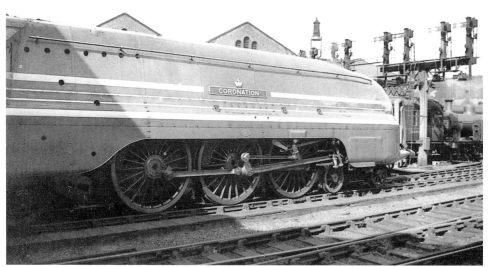

Stanier streamlined Pacific No. 6220 *Coronation* at Euston. Thought to be taken on 29th June, 1937. This partial view emphasises the smooth shape achieved.   *A.V.W. Mace Collection*

Coronation and 'Press' special train on arrival at Euston, 29th June, 1937.

A.V.W. Mace Collection

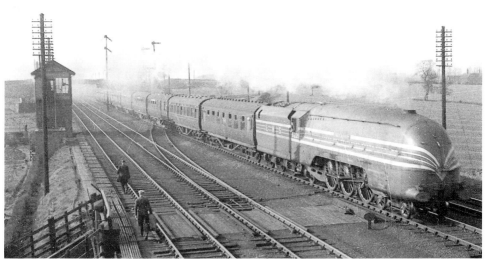

No. 6221 on up Euston express at Ashby Junction 1939. *R.S. Carpenter Collection*

Much testing was done on all Pacific types, here Stanier is to be found examining the results in the LMS dynamometer car on one of those tests. *W.M. Stanier*

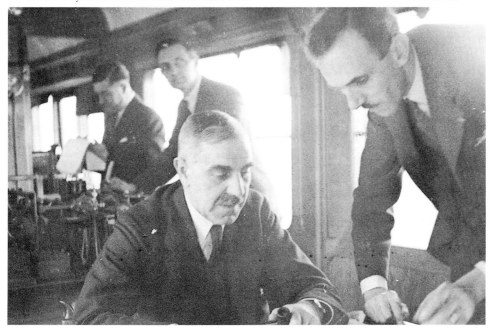

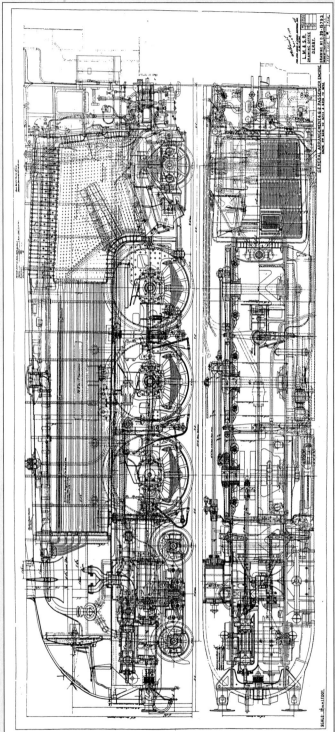

General arrangement of streamlined Pacific. Signed by Stanier (bottom right). *W.M. Stanier*

The boiler shop at Crewe. This view of a 'Coronation' class boiler under construction emphasises the massive superheater of 40 elements, the largest on any British locomotive in terms of surface area.
R.S. Carpenter Collection

The first batch of streamlined Pacifics under construction at Crewe, 28th April, 1938.
The Times

Unstreamlined Pacific No. 6234 *Duchess of Abercorn*.   *I.Mech.E.*

The Pacifics Developments

	1924	1925	1932	1932	1937
Designer	Hughes	Fowler	Stanier	Stanier	Stanier
No. of Cylinders	4	4	3	4	4
Bore	18 in.	16/23 in.	19 in.	16 in.	16 in.
Stroke	26 in.	26 in./26 in.	28 in.	28 in.	28 in.
Bogie wheels	3 ft 6 in.	3 ft 3 in.	3 ft 3 in.	3 ft 0 in.	3 ft 0 in.
Coupled wheels	6 ft 9 in.	6 ft 9 in.	6 ft 9 in.	6 ft 6 in.	6 ft 9 in.
Trailing wheels	3 ft 9 in.	3 ft 3 in.	4 ft 3 in.	3 ft 9 in.	3 ft 9 in.
Max boiler barrel dia.	5 ft 9 in.	5 ft 9 in.	6 ft 3 in.	6 ft 3 in.	6 ft 5 in.
Tube length	19 ft 0 in.	17 ft 0 in.	22 ft 0 in.	20 ft 9 in.	20 ft 3 in.
Tubes (large) no./dia.	32/5 in.	32/5 in.	?	16/5 in.	40/5 in.
Tubes (small) no./dia.	168/2 in.	172/2in.	?	170/2 in.	129/2 in.
Heating surface tubes	2,715 sq. ft	2,357 sq. ft	?	2,523 sq. ft	2,557 sq. ft
firebox	230 sq. ft	221 sq. ft	?	230 sq. ft	230 sq. ft
superheater	600 sq. ft	631 sq. ft	?	370 sq. ft	856 sq. ft
Total	3,545 sq. ft	3,209 sq. ft	?	3,123 sq. ft	3,643 sq. ft
Grate area	42 sq. ft	43.5 sq. ft	45 sq. ft	45 sq. ft	50 sq. ft
Boiler Pressure	180 psi	240 psi	250 psi	250 psi	250 psi
Tractive Effort	33,600 lb.	34,600 lb.	39,700 lb.	40,300 lb.	40,000 lb.

Notes:
(i) The 1924 Hughes and 1932 Stanier 3-cyl. never got beyond the drawing board.
(ii) The Fowler 1925 compound design was ordered but cancelled in 1926.
(iii) Of the Stanier 4-cyl. designs, 12 of the 1932 type were built, and 38 of the 1937 design built, of which 24 were originally streamlined.

Chapter Eight

The Class Fives and some Tanks

The London-Birmingham business service was always an important one for the LMS and the two-hour expresses had been in the hands of the Fowler 4-4-0 compounds which had been displaced, as they appeared, by the rebuilt 'Claughtons' ('Patriots').

Having permitted the continued production of the 'Patriot' 4-6-0s and, noting their good mechanical design and reliability in service, William decided that the design was worthy of development for this key service, which offered all sorts of facilities for the businessman, ranging from dining facilities to typists on board. And so the the first of two class '5' variants, both of which were to appear in 1934, was born. The first version had three-cylinders and was basically a 'Patriot' with a new taper boiler. It was this one that caused Stanier serious embarrassment - and it was serious. It unhappily combined those three bits of Swindon know-how that did not suit an LMS three-cylinder engine, namely low superheat, jumper blastpipe and smokebox deflector plates. The result was that the engines would not steam and D.C. Urie, who was then in charge of Motive Power and did not like these new-look engines anyway, not only refused (rightly) to use them on their design job, the Birmingham 2-hour expresses, but plugged away at a list of all their teething and other troubles, ranging from sticking smoke-box regulators to leaking top feeds. The Operating Manager, C.R. Byrom, joined in these complaints to their boss, Sir Ernest Lemon, who in turn joined with his fellow Vice-President, Sir Harold Hartley, in bringing great pressure on Stanier. He had a very worrying few months, being sustained by his own notable tenacity of purpose and by continuous understanding and support from the other Vice-President, Sir William Wood.

What had been right for Swindon was the result of a very specialised design philosophy written around a particular mix of standard components. Translating this into a different set of design parameters was bound to create some difficulties, and it is to the credit of Stanier that he allowed himself to be persuaded that not all Swindon ideas were transferable to other railways.

Thus, the 3-cylinder 4-6-0s had a chequered start to their lives. The need to deal swiftly with the steaming problem was brought to a head when No. 5665 *Lord Rutherford of Nelson*, a Crewe-built example of 1935 was rostered for a special to convey the gentleman of that name to Derby in order to open the new Research Department building in London Road. The train arrived with barely 100 psi on the gauge. The other passengers on this light, short, train included many of the Board and not a few questions were asked about the poor performance of this nearly-new locomotive.

Chambers was apparently despondent about this abysmal state of affairs and a wide-ranging programme of hit-and-miss attempts to cure this steaming problem was initiated involving no fewer than four designs of boiler, two grate sizes, four superheater layouts and six tube combinations being developed. Also there were two standards of blastpipe and two bogie wheelbases. All this between May 1934 and October 1936!

'Jubilee' No. 5630 is seen on a stopping train at Harpenden on 22nd April, 1935.   *J.M. Jarvis*

By 1937, the bugs had been ironed out and the '5XPs' were doing good work. One of the later examples, No. 5654 *Hood*, with separate top feed is found at Rugby Shed on 24th July, 1937.

J.M. Jarvis

'Jubilee' class 4-6-0 No. 5609 *Gilbert and Ellice Islands* at Cricklewood on 29th May, 1937.
R.S. Carpenter Collection

'5XP' No. 45678 *De Robeck*, built at Crewe in 1935 and seen here in early BR livery, was one of the first batch to have a domed boiler.
J.M. Jarvis

Crewe works in April 1935. A pair of 'Black Fives', Nos. 5021 and 5022, take shape. Next down the line is Pacific No. 6202, the 'Turbomotive'.   *A.V.W. Mace Collection*

A stopping service for a new 'Black Five', here No. 5042 calls at Harpenden 28th August, 1935.
J.M. Jarvis

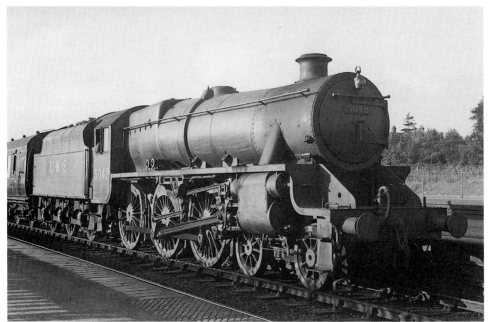

'Why couldn't Stanier realize at once,' people asked and still ask, 'what was wrong with the engines, and put them right?' To understand the answer to this one has to visualize the entire context. Stanier was introducing many novelties, most of which had at least one powerful antagonist. For example Derby drawing office did not like taper boilers, saying they were too expensive to make and looked wrong. Crewe works objected to the chore of finish-turning tyres previously rough-turned, saying it was a waste of money. However, Stanier insisted, pointing out that some tyre failures had been traced to coarse machining marks. The Derby Research Department had recently come up with this finding following their research into causes of accidents involving locomotive tyres cracking. We have already seen the Civil Engineer's objection to the 2-6-0 and Pacifics as regards clearances. Stanier had to win all these over.

Riddles spotted that the blast was never quite adequate and suggested a reduction to the blastpipe diameter and the removal of the deflector plates in order to improve the draughting. From the trials of boiler features mentioned above a combination was found which, with Riddles suggestions, satisfied the steaming problem, but the credibility of the leadership of the Derby LDO had been dented by this episode and from now on we find the influence of Coleman, now at Crewe, becoming predominant, and he was soon to replace Chambers as chief draughtsman. The performance of the engines was further enhanced when the superheater was changed to a high degree type. All this took time, during which the complaints continued. A total of 191 made up the class, all being constructed between 1934 and 1938. Stanier had no experience of three-cylinder design prior to this, as the GWR was strictly a two- or four-cylinder line. It just goes to show how a change to three cylinders can, if applied with sundry other changes, upset steaming properties. The MR faction of the LMS had always had a philosophy of using three cylinders instead of four on the grounds of cost and weight, but for utter simplicity one cannot better the two-cylinder layout, despite the worry of hammer-blow it entailed.

The entry into service of the '5XP' 4-6-0 was a slow process. Relegated to minor duties, such examples as had been put on the road were troublesome steamers much disliked by the crews. Several examples sat in Crewe Stock Shed in storage to await the final decision as to modification status. Meantime many of the intended rosters for them were catered for by the 'Patriots' which had proved themselves reliable and speedy. Also, the occasional compound was to be found supporting the 'Patriots' but these were beginning to struggle with some loads.

The class '5' two-cylinder version, however, was a success from the start, even with the low degree superheating. The 'Black Five', as it became generally known, was really an LMS version of the GWR 'Hall' mixed-traffic type having the same 6 ft driving wheel but with a tractive effort of 24,455 lb. as against the 'Hall' value of 27,275lb. However, the class '5s' cylinder stroke was two inches less than the 'Hall'.

The way in which the Horwich DO had handled the 2-6-0 resulted in the 2-cylinder 4-6-0 being given to them by Stanier. Again Coleman and his contract men produced the drawings in record time. As they were finishing off, an order for 50 was placed with the Vulcan Foundry. In fact, it has been speculated that

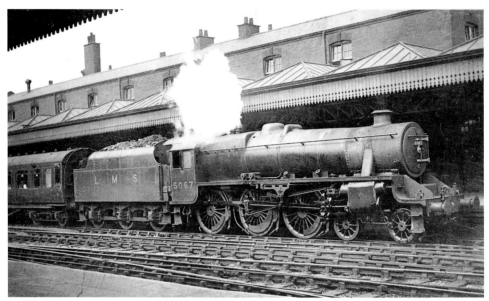

The hooter in action on 'Black Five' No. 5067 at Nottingham Midland in the 1930s.

John Scott-Morgan

'Black Five' No. 5187 at Kettering with a semi-fast passenger train in the 1930s.

John Scott-Morgan

some of the final detail design was completed by that company. The Vulcan Foundry chief draughtsman was Charles Finlayson, brother of 'Jock' Finlayson at the Southern Railway Eastleigh works, and so it is not surprising that there appeared to be a similarity between the Urie 'H15' and the new class '5' 4-6-0.

The success of the 'Black Five', as the new design was to be dubbed, made Stanier implement what he had planned for some time now, the redistribution of his drawing office teams. In 1935 Coleman was decisively promoted to take charge of the DO at Crewe, being replaced at Horwich by Martin from Crewe. Stanier had long been at odds with Martin and wished to sideline him. Coleman brought with him and placed at Crewe the best of his team built up at Horwich, a wise decision as it gave him some backing when the Crewe DO was involved in delegated design work.

By now Stanier clearly wished to get Coleman in charge at Derby, so, in 1936, Chambers was 'promoted' to a personal assistant rôle in the CME's office at Euston, being replaced as chief draughtsman by Coleman, who had by now been given a line diagram for a 2-8-0.

'Black Fives' were to be the second most prolific of Stanier types on the LMS, with 842 being built in a production cycle through to 1951. Two outside contractors, the Vulcan Foundry (100) and Armstrong Whitworth (225), were involved in this, together with Crewe, Derby and Horwich.

The mixed-traffic capabilities of these locomotives soon found them operating over the whole system on a wide range of duties from express passenger to branch freight. The simple layout, with external valve gear, made everything get-at-able for maintenance, and Urie must have found the ease of servicing similar to his father's 4-6-0s designed for the LSWR in 1917. Robert Urie had pioneered this format in those early days and it only remained for Stanier to follow his design and marry it to all the best in Swindon steam-raising technology and long travel valve gear. Maunsell, on the Southern had got very close to this ideal in his 'S15' 4-6-0 based on Urie's design.

Even though the 'Black Fives' were performing adequately with the initial 14 element low degree superheater, Stanier agreed that an improvement in the superheater area would be beneficial, and progressively they were given 28 element superheaters.

The initial analysis of the low degree superheating test figures were not exactly a true picture of events, for it was admitted by F.J. Pepper of the Derby drawing office that some of the early figures were 'leant on' before being sent to Stanier. This effect of minimising the ill-effects of low superheat was a crude attempt to please the CME, but did not carry much weight as continued complaints came from the Running side to make William realise that not all was as implied. He shrewdly accepted these early findings whilst looking at the overall picture in the context of running performance.

Unfortunately, much of the complaining reached him via Hartley, rather than his own staff, and anyone who has experienced a similar chain of passing comments, knows that sometimes data gets embellished or distorted *en route*. Stanier was unaccustomed to the separation from the Running side he had enjoyed at Swindon and throughout this troubling time no one heard him blame anyone but himself. He was, however, gradually getting to grips with the

Already 15 years old, 'Black Five' No. 45002, one of the initial 1935 batch, is looking like new on Rugby Shed on 13th May, 1950.

J.M. Jarvis

situation and was soon in a position to overcome all the shortcomings created by his radical change to the locomotive design thinking on the LMS. Matters were now so cut and dried with the introduction of all the Swindon ideas, that all partisanship seemed superfluous and the design teams were more in tune with their new CME's philosophy. One factor which helped all this was the installation of Coleman as chief draughtsman at Derby.

Perhaps the best example of the benefits of high-degree superheating is to be found in the following table which compares the 'Black Five' results with 14 and 21 element superheaters.

Engine No.	5067	5079	% change
S/heater Elements	14	21	
Train weight	292 tons	292 tons	
Coal consumption	49.5 lb./mile	43.7 lb./mile	-12.0
lb./dbhp	3.97	3.23	-18.5
lb./ton mile	0.098	0.085	-13.0
Water gal./mile	38.2	32.8	-14.0

One day late 1934 found William in No. 4 Shed at Derby. On one of his regular visits some query had arisen concerning the superheater elements on a recently arrived 'Black Five'. Works staff were ordered to remove the self-cleaning plates to enable the CME to clamber inside and inspect the elements himself. Despite the fact that there was still residual pressure in the boiler, William gamely climbed up and fitted his tall frame into the warm confines of the box.

The London, Tilbury & Southend arm of the LMS was, by now, in dire need of more powerful locomotives to replace some of the 4-4-2 tanks struggling with heavy commuter trains. William looked at the existing Fowler 2-6-4T, which was still in production in 1933/4 and decided that a three-cylinder version should fill the requirement. Three cylinders were chosen as it was thought this would provide a high acceleration on the stopping services. However, subsequent experience showed that the Fowler two-cylinder type was capable of equal performance. For the three-cylinder layout the Derby drawing office departed from the divided drive of the 'Scots' and 'Patriots', and went for a middle axle drive from all cylinders. Whether or not a conjugated valve gear was ever suggested is not known, probably not, for Stanier had his personal misgivings about such an arrangement and most certainly would have vetoed it. Nevertheless, the 37 three-cylinder 2-6-4Ts were liked by the enginemen and were to be the prime power for the Southend services for many years, The only other major changes on top of the conversion to a three-cylinder configuration of the Fowler design were the taper boiler, top feed and revised cab.

When it was realised that this 2-6-4T would be just as capable (and lighter and cheaper) with two cylinders, all future locomotives of this type were built as such, beginning in 1935 and remaining in production until 1943, when their number reached 206. Fowler had permitted the introduction of long travel, long lap valves on his original design, which Stanier left largely alone in the interest of standardisation with the 125 examples built before the Stanier version. The 206 was not to be the final total, however, as a further 277 were to be built from

LTSR 4-4-2T No. 2135 with, in the background, the Stanier 2-6-4T which was to supersede it.
H.F. Wheeller Collection

A brand-new 2-6-4T (3-cyl) No. 2521 is being turned at Nottingham London Road, 1934.
R.S. Carpenter Collection

1945 to 1951. They included some improvements, having self-cleaning smokeboxes, rocking grates and self-emptying ashpans.

As all this development proceeded, news of problems was beginning to filter through from the running sheds, although much of this was of the maintenance staff's own making, for they were doing some positively idiotic things to his engines, such as screwing down the adjusters on the top feed clacks, thus shutting off the feed to the boiler. Stanier could hardly believe it when this madness actually grew worse, and in 1936 Derby issued a large diagram explaining to shed fitters 'why NOT (Derby's capitals) to screw down studs protruding from top feed clack boxes.' His comparitively rare rebukes usually came when someone failed in what he considered a straightforward task - as at Derby in January 1935 when, having stayed overnight at the Midland Hotel, he walked into the erecting shop soon after 8 am and expressed annoyance that the head foreman was not yet present. Later, when inspecting the paint shop, where one of the new 'Jubilees' was being finished, the foreman unwisely fished for a compliment. This tactic always slightly annoyed Stanier and it chanced that some hand-wheels had been painted black, which he disliked. 'But the crews would never keep them polished,' protested the foreman, and got the reply 'If it looks smart to start with, they will take pride in keeping it smart.' Stanier must have repeated this story at a family gathering, because from it there came a family saying often repeated by nieces and cousins: 'Uncle Will says, if it looks nice to start with . . .' There became no need to finish the phrase.

William's round of socialising was quite modest but he never let his worries and frustrations impinge on his family - they were strictly for working hours. A typical social visit was to the Bulleids for tea one afternoon, where the family was greeted as 'Stamer' by Mrs Bulleid. William glossed over this early glitch, but not Nelle who said firmly, 'The name is Stanier'. They were treated to a 3-reel film made at Derby by Anthony Bulleid, then completing his apprenticeship there. The film had a strong railway background with much action on and around a Midland compound, which prompted William to ask, 'Why didn't you use one of the new engines?' This response, Anthony recalled many years after the event, reminded him of the time his grandmother presented him with a red toy engine and H.A. Ivatt, his grandfather, gave it one look and asked 'Why Midland?'

With the undoubted success of the 2-6-4 tanks, a further design exercise was carried out using the Fowler 2-6-2T as a baseline, Again the changes were taper boiler, top feed and cab, plus long travel valve gear which the original Fowler types did not have. However, the resulting engine was, perhaps the least successful of all Stanier designs. It was under-boilered, as had been the Fowler version, and as such was an indifferent performer. 139 were built at Derby and Crewe between 1935 and 1938.

ATC raised its head in 1936, with Stanier receiving a request from Hartley to get together with Hudd, the Signals Engineer, and decide on its application to the LMS. William's involvement in the introduction of ATC 30 years ago on the GWR had confirmed his belief in the principle. A trial set-up was planned and installed on the busy Southend line. The system chosen was different to the GWR approach in that a direct electrical contact with a ramp could not be

A further example of the 2-cylinder 2-6-4T, No. 2494 at Watford Shed on 10th July, 1937. There appears to be a turbo-generator installed.
R.G. Jarvis

Stanier's 2-cylinder 2-6-4T No. 2546 caught on stopping train at Harpenden, August 1936.
J.M. Jarvis

The 2-6-2T was never all that popular or successful. Even though this view of No. 105 was taken in 1947, domeless boilers were still around. Bournville Shed 10th June, 1947. *J.M. Jarvis*

The lower boiler mountings show that this 2-6-2T, No. 163, has been rebuilt with a larger boiler, which made little difference to its performance. Derby 1948.   *J.M. Jarvis*

The ill-fated *Fury*, still sporting indicating shelters, and in steam, outside Derby works, 1931.
          R.G. Jarvis

guaranteed during hard frosts on the high altitude lines such as Shap Fell. The alternative magnetic proximity detector developed and suggested by Hudd was used instead. However, the task of installing ATC over the whole of the LMS was curtailed by the approach of the war. With limited resources (for the LMS profitability was insufficient to provide the necessary capital in one fell swoop) only the initial Southend line system was completed. By late 1938 it was found possible to dispense with fogmen on this line.

Following its disastrous accident in 1930 the sole example of the Fowler experimental high-pressure 4-6-0 *Fury* had languished in storage at Derby. William had improvements planned for the 'Royal Scot' and 'Patriot' classes, even though these locomotives were doing well on the LMS. However, such changes as were initially made were more to do with the riding qualities rather than the boilers, which were good steamers. So, bearing in mind that these express types were still relatively new, particularly the 'Patriots', there was not much of a case to promote expensive rebuilding at a time when so many other new classes were appearing. However, to prove his case for eventual reboilering, opportunity presented itself in the presence of *Fury*. As this engine had identical frames and motion to the 'Royal Scot' class, he saw the rebuilding as an opportunity to produce more or less a prototype for that exercise. A single example of the boiler planned for the 'Royal Scot' was installed, with standard cylinders to replace the compound ones of *Fury*. Although the resulting locomotive was not exactly as the actual conversions were to be, it showed a marked improvement in steaming which was to eventually to transform an already excellent locomotive (the 'Royal Scot') into an outstanding one. The boiler design for this rebuild was done at Crewe by G.R. Nicholson, one of Coleman's transfers from Horwich, who had been trained at the Yorkshire Engine Co. and then gaining further work experience in South America before returning to the UK.

The rebuild of *Fury*, No. 46170, used to prove the 'Royal Scot rebuild'. Although the rebuilding was carried out in 1935, the 'Scots' had to wait until 1943 for the commencement of the class rebuilding exercise.   *J.M. Jarvis*

However, it was to be some years before funds were allocated for the rebuilding of the complete class. Not until 1942 was the authority given for 20 to be so treated. It was 1955 before the whole class was rebuilt.

The 'Patriot' rebuilding with a taper boiler came much later and only ever covered 18 of the 52 in the class. The remainder soldiered on with their parallel boilers until withdrawal in the early 1960s.

Whilst all the trials and iterations of the classes '5' and '5XP' were under way, additional pressure on Stanier appeared in the form of a request for some specialised information. The rise to power of Hitler in 1933 awoke some to the strong possibility of future conflict. As the railways had been such an important player in the production of munitions in the 1914-18 war, the subject of a drive to plan some work towards rearmament appeared on the LMS Board's agenda. Sir Harold Hartley called on Stanier in 1934 to carry out a survey of all LMS machine tools likely to be suitable for munitions work. The summary of this was to be supplied to the Committee of Imperial Defence which was assessing the capacity of the railway works should they be needed in the future. Derby, Crewe, Horwich and St Rollox were included in this survey. As the 1930s progressed, preparations were planned for a wide-ranging effort in munitions work which was to be proved a vital ingredient in the war to come.

A batch of three 'Black Fives' arrives at Crewe works yard in 1936 from Armstrong, Whitworth who built no fewer than 225.   *R.S. Carpenter Collection*

Chapter Nine

The Freight Scene and India

When Stanier became CME, much of the LMS heavy freight matters were catered for by a large fleet of 0-8-0s, some of ex-LNWR and ex-L&YR pre-Grouping vintage, with well over 700 of these ageing engines in service. There were also 175 of the Fowler class '7F' of 1929, the final numbers of which were being turned out of Crewe in 1932. To back up these large engines there were over 700 of the reliable Fowler class '4F' 0-6-0 which could often be found working in pairs on the heavy freight tasks. Finally, there were the 33 Garratts.

Minor freight duties were largely in the hands of some 1,500 other 0-6-0s of the other main constituents of the LMS, many of Victorian antiquity.

Although the Fowler 0-8-0 was a new design, derived from the LNWR class 'G2', it had its Achilles' heel of the inadequate '4F' axleboxes. The 175 in service worked only fairly adequately because of this, but did have the advantage of long travel, long lap, valve gear and, whilst it showed considerably better coal and water consumption than the older class 'G2', the boxes were to plague it throughout its life. The LNWR and L&YR 0-8-0s were sturdier with adequate bearings and the LNWR variant, the 'G2', was in fact to outlive the newer Fowler '7F'.

Heavy freight motive power was still under review in 1932 and William's first thoughts obviously drifted to the GWR 2-8-0 layout. Now, Fowler had produced a 2-8-0 design in 1914 for the Somerset and Dorset Joint Railway, but this suffered from the dual problems of '4F' axleboxes and short travel valves. Only 11 examples had been built. This relatively old design was discarded early on in the search for a possible starting point.

In the 1933 Locomotive Committee meetings Stanier proposed, and got authority for, two experimental 2-8-0s for the 1934 programme. In fact the initial batch totalled 12, and these were built at Crewe in 1935. The Stanier '8F' was to become the largest single class under his design leadership, although of the 852 built, 133 were for the War Department orders. For once these engines had proved their worth on the LMS, it came as no surprise that the WD chose it for quantity production to meet the urgent needs of World War II motive power; as had the Robinson 2-8-0 of the Great Central Railway been adopted for WD use in World War I.

The original line diagram for the 2-8-0, produced at Euston, incorporated a class '5' boiler, but when Coleman ordered a weight distribution it was found to be too heavy on the two rear coupled axles. The diagram had been done using the Swindon layout and the shorter firebox of this compared to the class '5' had produced a weight shift to the rear. The answer was to move the boiler forward and upward, the latter needed for the ashpan to clear the third coupled axle, hence the distinctive high-pitched boiler on the 2-8-0 that resulted.

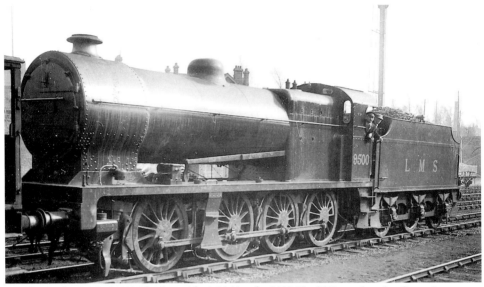

The Fowler 0-8-0 of 1929. The first of the initial batch of 100, No. 9500, produced at Crewe is seen at Manchester that year.   *R.S. Carpenter Collection*

The Fowler 0-8-0s were to be seen in large numbers over the central area of the LMS. Here two are found at Crewe South when nearly new.   *R.S. Carpenter Collection*

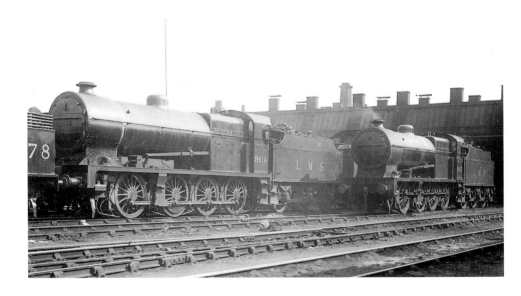

2-8-0 Comparisons

Designer	Churchward	Fowler	Stanier
Year	1903	1914	1935
Cylinders (2)	18 x 30	21 x 28	18 x 28
Boiler length	14 ft 10 in.	11 ft 11 in.	11 ft 10 in.
Dia. at front	4 ft 10 in.	5 ft 3 in.	5 ft 0 in.
Dia. at rear	5 ft 6 in.	5 ft 3 in.	5 ft 8 in.
Tube heating surface	1,608 sq. ft	1,323 sq. ft	1,479 sq. ft
Firebox heating surface	150 sq. ft	148 sq. ft	171 sq. ft
Superheater	265 sq. ft	374 sq. ft	245 sq. ft
Pressure	225 psi	180 psi	225 psi
Coupled wheels	4 ft 7 in.	4 ft 7 in.	4 ft 8 in.
Wheelbase of coupled wheels	16 ft 10 in.	17 ft 6 in.	17 ft 3 in.
Tractive effort	35,380 lb.	35,392 lb.	32,438 lb.
Weight of engine	75 t. 10 cwt	68 t. 11 cwt	70 t. 10 cwt
Weight of tender	40 t. 0 cwt	42 t. 13 cwt	54 t. 13 cwt

Reference to the above table shows clearly the Churchward influence on the Stanier design. Even though the GWR locomotive dated from 1903, the design advances were sufficient for it to still be found in production up to 1942, a prodigious 39-year run! The Fowler design, though nominally of similar power to the GWR design, had a parallel boiler in addition to the other shortcomings mentioned earlier and, as such, never had a chance of being updated.

The class '8F' was to have a long production run, becoming one of the few types to be operated on all four main railways in the UK, and certainly the only class to be built by all the railways. Its straightforward two-cylinder design made maintenance easy and a low axle loading of 16 tons gave an excellent route availability.

For the easier light freight duties Stanier kept the Fowler '4F' in production, building batches totalling 45 up to 1941. With the pressure of other work there was no opportunity to design a better mid-range all-rounder, and it made economic sense to perpetuate this standard class, of which such a large number were in service by 1932. New 0-6-0s were a dying breed, this classic layout reaching its zenith with Bulleid's 'Q1' on the Southern in 1940. Although William had ordered the Derby drawing office to carry out a 2-6-0 redesign of the successful Fowler 2-6-4T and some schemes for a more modern 0-6-0, the Operating Department pressured for additional '4Fs' as being the ideal answer to their requirements. This was, in retrospect, one example of a retrograde aspect concerning LMS locomotive affairs which slipped through Stanier's net.

Total 0-6-0 numbers were in excess of 2,200 in Stanier's time, namely over a quarter of the total fleet of all types. To replace the majority, if his scrap-and-build policy was to be fully followed would have been a colossal task absorbing a vast amount of capital, so the current fleet soldiered on for many more years, with many taken into British Railways' stock at Nationalisation

A measure of the effectiveness of Stanier's big re-stocking programme can be gauged by the change in the total number of locomotives which, prior to his arrival was not far short of 10,000. By 1938 this number had reduced to 7,688, and this latter fleet was doing the same work, if not more, than the earlier number.

The GWR 2-8-0 of Churchward, here No. 2814 is caught at Tyseley in 1931.

R.S. Carpenter Collection

The SDJR 2-8-0 of Fowler, No. 9678 at Bath, 1930.   *R.S. Carpenter Collection*

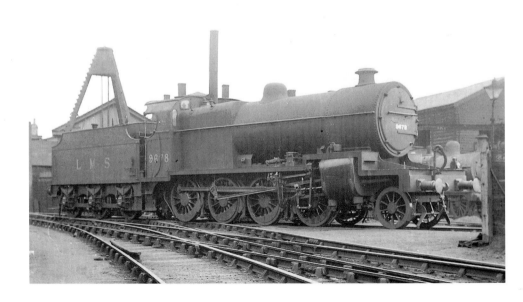

Much of the lighter tasks were allocated to the Johnson '3F' 0-6-0. Here No. 3763, rebuilt in 1905, shunts some horseboxes at Nottingham Midland. *c.*1930. *John Scott-Morgan Collection*

The '4F' of Fowler was to live through Stanier's days even being produced in small numbers up to 1941. No. 4278 is photographed at Derby Shed looking as though it has paid a recent visit to the paint shop to receive this experimental BR lettering scheme. *J.M. Jarvis*

An '8F' under construction at Crewe, 1935.   *R.S. Carpenter Collection*

The Stanier 2-8-0 on a typical task. No. 8064 on a northbound goods at Breadsall Crossing near Allestree, Derby, 1st June, 1947.   *J.M. Jarvis*

1937 had seen a restructuring in the CME's Department, in that Fairburn was promoted to the position of Deputy Chief Mechanical Engineer and Electrical Engineer and no fewer than four Principal Assistants created:

Locomotives	H.G. Ivatt
Carriages and Wagons	J. Purves
Electrical Engineering	F.A. Harper
Outdoor Machinery	J. Boyd

Ivatt was the son of H.A. Ivatt, the eminent CME of the former Great Northern Railway, and was himself to become CME of the LMS in 1946. He replaced R. Riddles who was sent to Scotland as Mechanical and Electrical Engineer.

Stanier's expertise was, by now, becoming well-known throughout the upper echelons of the railway hierarchy. So it was natural, with his wide experience on design, production and running aspects, that he be selected as the person to cover such matters on a committee of experts being assembled to visit India to report on the state of that country's railway network.

The UK party consisting of Sir Ralph Wedgwood and William Stanier, accompanied by Sir Ralph's assistant, M.A. Forbes Smith, left England in early November 1936 and arrived in Bombay on the 19th of that month. Their task was formidable - to inspect the conditions, financial and technical, of the Indian railways on behalf of the Indian Government. The Indian railways were extensive, some 36,000 miles of track in place, of three gauges; 5 ft 6 in., metre and narrow (largely 2 ft), so this was not going to be a short visit.

From Bombay they travelled to Delhi to discuss their planned itinerary with senior officials of the Indian Government and the railways involved. The travelling, in a special train, commenced with a return to Bombay after an initial foray to Lahore to cover the North Western Railway's territory. At Bombay, on the 12th December, the final member of the Committee joined them. This was Mr H. Cheadle, the Chief Traffic Manager of the South African Railways, and whose expertise on narrow gauge matters was to be invaluable.

Over the next six weeks, apart from a break over Christmas, they travelled throughout the Indian peninsular. Over 7,000 miles were covered in that time, and William added a further 2,000 to that total in his frequent diversions to workshops and sheds for inspections of the repair and running side of matters.

There were certainly problems on the Indian railways which, like the UK lines, had suffered during the war years through high utilisation and were starved of much capital investment which had been exacerbated by the early 1930s depression.

William found an intolerably high incidence of hot axle-boxes on locomotives, at most sheds hardly a day went by without a locomotive having to be lifted for attention. He fully agreed with the comments heard concerning the rectification of bad lubrication practices, and also on the need to improve devices which excluded the ingress of dust, always a problem in hot, dry, climates.

As regards the goods stock, there was a large number of wagons out of service with broken buffers, indicative of vigorous shunting, and much old stock was becoming worn out. Repairs took too long and there were many signs of defective supervision.

He addressed the Indian Branch of the Institution of Locomotive Engineers on their urgent need for practical experience in exam-qualified engineers; but the trip had depressed him in that engineering came a poor second to socio-political influences such as the relentless pressure put on railway employees by relatives wanting jobs on the railway.

From the completion of their travelling on 20th January, 1937, the committee prepared their critical report in Delhi and submitted it to the Government authorities. On 20th February they returned to Bombay and sailed for home to pick up the reins again.

Stanier continued with his plans to produce a new, improved, version of his Pacific in addition to addressing a burning issue concerning the testing of both new and existing locomotives.

Although locomotive testing was carried out on each new type as it emerged, the LMS method used of dynamometer car plus indicator shelters was far from ideal. Swindon, of course, had the 'A' shop plant and could, under controlled conditions, simulate the ideal running environment. Collett still disliked liaison with other railways and there seemed little point in asking for his co-operation.

By the mid-1930s Stanier was of the opinion that a modern locomotive testing plant would be of great value. He had the case of the Swindon plant as an example, and the argument around this was bolstered by the fact that, a few years earlier, Collett had updated this facility such that it could now absorb the full power of any GWR locomotive - previously it had been restricted to 500 horsepower output, making its use extemely limited. The cost of a test plant to the LMS itself would have been prohibitive in the current climate of low profitability, and so, after discussion with Gresley, a proposal for a joint LMS/LNER test plant was agreed and the two Boards voted funds for its construction, the site chosen being at Rugby. Up to that time Gresley had sent locomotives to the test station at Vitry in France, and the possibility of having a home plant was attractive. Also, an important fact, as with the Gresley streamlined Pacifics, the streamlined casing of the new 'Coronation' class meant that indicating shelters could not be set up for on the road tests. Only a static facility would allow that sort of testing. Additionally Stanier had always preferred to have any testing done on home ground and had never wished to follow Gresley's lead. By early 1939, construction was advanced and some of the specialised test gear ordered from the Swiss company of Amsler. Progress was slow, however, and with R.C. Bond installed as Superintendent, it was hoped to make this facility operational in 1940. In addition to the order for Amsler test gear for the plant, an additional order for new dynamometer car gear was placed, as it made sense to re-equip this with equipment compatible with that to be employed on the static tests. The delivery arrived at Derby shortly before war broke out and was put carefully into storage.

However, international events were to result in a cessation of the development for some years, but before we pass on to that time, Stanier's other developmental work and a further India visit need to be addressed after a brief assessment of carriage developments.

Chapter Ten

The Coaching Stock of the LMS

The Midland Railway had always prided itself on the high standard of workmanship and comfort of its carriage stock: 'The finest in the Country' as their publicity people proudly proclaimed. Also, in the 50 years preceding Grouping the MR had only employed three Carriage Superintendents, the last of which, R.W. Reid, became the first LMS Carriage Superintendent. And so it was natural that all new carriage stock was based on Midland coaches. Reid had been elevated to Vice-President of the LMS in 1927, but died two years later. Since then the carriage affairs had been dealt with by E.J.H. Lemon who had retained this aspect upon his temporary one year placement as CME, prior to the arrival of Stanier. It was therefore natural, when William took over as CME at Euston, that he was to include the carriage affairs as part of his department, as indeed he had been used to on the GWR.

At Grouping the LNWR had bequeathed some 5,000 coaches to the LMS, including a large number of sleeping and dining cars and the large 12-wheeled corridor coaches built for the Scottish services. There was also a large fleet of antiques dating from 1880-90 included in the 5,000. Many of these old four- and six-wheeled variants needed replacing by the LMS as soon as that railway came into being, as did the older of the bogie stock.

In 1928 came a new layout for express stock, which employed end doors in place of the side doors for each compartment. Windows could thus be enlarged to single picture windows for the compartments of the corridor stock and which were also suitable for the open vestibule stock being introduced.

In 1932, as he began to input his thoughts into the wide-ranging CME's responsibilities, Stanier ordered that carriage construction methods be investigated in detail to ascertain whether any savings in cost and weight might be feasible. Some 106 small parts per coach were identified as capable of elimination by altering the design slightly. One significant feature was the introduction of welding to the solebar of pillar brackets which had previously to be bolted to a timber framing, itself bolted to the underframe.

The weight saving obtained by changing to welded construction compared to the previous riveted assembly for both underframes and bogies brought about a total weight reduction of one ton for a standard carriage. Some of the first vehicles to employ this new technique were 26 first class sleeping-cars of 69 ft length mounted on six-wheel bogies

Stanier then expanded the use of steel panels on wooden framing becoming standard for the sides to the ends and roof. Lengths were standardised at 57 ft, although there were some special cases demanding carriages of other lengths, and a modular form of construction in jigs expanded to cover all new carriage stock construction.

One feature of Stanier coach stock was the greater comfort for third class passengers, for individual compartments were now fitted out for six passengers instead of eight as previously although, by retracting the arm-rests the latter

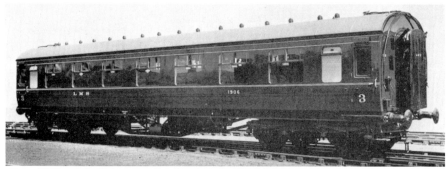

Above: LMS standard passenger coach as produced under Stanier. *Below:* A partially finished standard passenger coach. *(Both) I.Mech.E.*

The Stanier welded bogie for standard coach stock. *I.Mech.E.*

number could be accommodated. As regards the open vestibule stock, many were fitted with tables between the facing sets of seats and were employed as additional seating for the dining cars on the longer runs. Some of the Birmingham, Liverpool and Manchester business expresses often had as many as four dining vehicles, as dining trade was substantial. Even in BR days, the author can recollect a quite affordable dinner in such a vehicle on the Leicester run behind, usually, a 'Black Five' or 'Jubilee'.

The seating on LMS carriages was, on the whole, quite comfortable, for as Stanier arrived, a device created by the LMS Research Department at Derby, going under the delightful name of the 'mechanical bottom', pounded up and down on sample seats to test them for durability. Even for suburban stock the LMS commuter was in far more comfort than those coming into Kings Cross or Liverpool Street in the sit-up-and-beg conditions of the Gresley Quad-Arts or Quint-Arts respectively.

In 1936 Stanier ordered the design of articulated stock in an effort to reduce train weights and in 1937 there appeared 110 vestibule coaches built as 55 sets of articulated pairs. Additionally, 33 non-corridor coaches in ten 3-car articulated sets were turned out. With bogies accounting for 31 per cent of the weight of a passenger coach, it made sense to go for articulation if possible. However, with the prevailing LMS policy of not building carriage stock in complete train sets, this attempt at reducing weight and cost got no further than this limited number.

However, one development did appear to offer considerable potential, that of lightweight all-metal construction. Stanier ordered some research effort to be channelled into this, starting with a diesel set and some new stock for the Wirral and Liverpool-Southport suburban electric lines.

These new electric sets were quite an advance on the sets they were to replace. For the Liverpool-Southport operation many of them dated back to the conversion of the line to electric traction in 1904. These new products employed high-density seating and had air-operated sliding doors, a thoroughly modern design.

As early as 1933 consideration of welding techniques for coach construction was being promoted by Stanier. The electric arc method was the preferred type and was to be introduced on a large scale for the construction of new carriage stock. The new electric sets were built as all-welded assemblies which resulted in a weight saving of nearly seven tons for the motor cars and 1½ tons for the trailer cars, when compared to the older methods of construction. Furthermore, the passenger capacity for a three-car set was increased by a total of 19 over the old sets, and this for a much greater degree of comfort than hitherto.

With the advent of the 'Coronation' class of streamlined Pacifics some new carriages were needed for the 'Coronation Scot' train in 1937. In fact, the first train sets were not new coaches but rebuilds of existing stock. One unique feature of all 'Coronation' stock was the pressure ventilation (air conditioning), each coach having its individual hot and cold air units, the coaches being identified by the external air ducts running along the roofs. When it was decided to send a display train to the New York World Fair in 1939, a complete new train of eight coaches was built consisting of three 2-car articulated units

Lightweight electric stock under construction.   *I.Mech.E.*

A finished motor coach for the new electric stock.   *I.Mech.E.*

plus two conventional bogie brake vehicles. One further notable feature of the carriage stock was the fitting of fairings between the carriages to reduce eddy drags. This all goes to show that the LMS Research Department was fully up to scratch in the application of the latest aerodynamic technology in railway vehicle design. The total tare weight of this train was 262 tons 10 cwt and would have been 289 tons 13 cwt had standard all bogie construction been used. This set was never used in the UK as it was to be stranded in America by the outbreak of the war.

A graphic example as to the potential weight saving available by the modernization of the constructional techniques instigated by Stanier is given below:

Weights of Third Class Corridor Coaches

	Weight	Tare per Passenger
Riveted Standard	30 t. 6 cwt 0 q.	1,615 lb.
Welded Standard	28 t. 16 cwt 0 q.	1,535 lb.
Welded Lightweight	25 t. 19 cwt 3 q.	1,385 lb.

Since 1932, therefore, considerable advances in coach construction had been introduced under Stanier and many of the new techniques were to continue into the days of British Railways, as did many of the carriages themselves. These Stanier carriage developments were equal, if not better, than the early BR examples, particularly as regards their riding qualities. The introduction of air-conditioning on the 'Coronation Scot' stock was most certainly a big step forward in the UK (the LNER also having introduced it in the same year for its own 'Coronation' express between London and Edinburgh) and was only to reappear as BR developed its standard carriage stock starting in the 1950s.

Some specialised carriage stock appeared just before the war which must be recorded here. In 1936, Stanier received a suggestion from H.I. Andrew of the LMS Research Department for constant speed testing of locomotives by the employment of braking vehicles in the test train. This principle stemmed from some research by Lomonosoff in Russia which had been successfully applied in Poland and Germany. A set of three special vehicles, based on the standard carriage stock, was eventually built, capable of being used singly or in multiple. Any variation in speed normally caused by up or down gradients could be eliminated, thus permitting constant speed testing which gave much better results. For a fuller description of this equipment, by none other than Stanier himself, see Appendix Four.

The last steam shunting engine obtained by the LMS was this Sentinel 0-4-0 No. 7192, delivered in 1934 and seen here on 19th July, 1936 at Crewe South.   *H.F. Wheeller Collection*

Diesel shunter No. 7054 is seen at Derby on 25th April, 1937. It was built by the Hunslet Engine Co. of Leeds (Works No. 1724) in 1934, and was withdrawn by the LMS in 1943. It was sold on for use in industry and was not scrapped until 1974.   *H.F. Wheeller Collection*

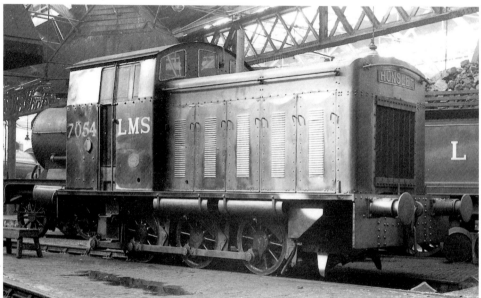

Chapter Eleven

Diesels, India Again and War

It was the LMS that began the introduction of diesel power on the British railways, commencing with its application for shunting work. When Stanier took office as CME a development at Derby in the form of a diesel-hydraulic shunter was under way. This was a collaborative project between the Derby LDO and the Derby firm of Haslam-Newton who were basically electrical engineers. The agreement was that if the LMS provided an engine chassis and body, Haslam-Newton would provide the power equipment. The result was No. 1831, which had a converted chassis of an old Johnson 0-6-0T upon which was mounted a Paxman diesel engine with hydraulic transmission for a jackshaft drive to the three coupled axles. The power unit was enclosed in a van-like body incorporating cabs at each end. It proved troublesome, the Achilles' heel being the fluid drive. The interest at top levels was insufficient to provide the necessary impetus to iron out the problems and this, coupled with a lack of money available, ensured that the project died. However, a step towards modernisation had been made and in a relatively short time, diesel power came on the agenda again.

This time it was through a borrowed Hunslet diesel-mechanical unit working at Leeds which was showing promise. Sir Harold Hartley authorised the expenditure of £30,000 for further experimental work on diesel shunting locomotives. Accordingly it was decided to purchase up to 10 machines of similar type. This order actually ended up for eight, all 0-6-0s, from Hunslet (4), Hudswell, Clarke (2), Harland and Wolff (builders of the *Titanic*) (1) and Armstrong, Whitworth (1). The Armstrong, Whitworth example differed in that it was a diesel-electric type, with a 250 hp engine (the others had ranged from 150 hp to 180 hp). A further single example was ordered from Hawthorn, Leslie in late 1934.

It was around this time that the LMS Electrical Engineer, Lt Col F.A. Cortez-Leigh was due for retirement. Hartley, an academic himself, looked around for someone with a similar background and with industrial experience and found C.E. Fairburn at English Electric.

By the time the diesel shunters were being delivered, William had added Fairburn to his team as Chief Electrical Engineer. Fairburn, after acquiring three Firsts at Oxford, had joined the Midland Railway as a pupil of Henry Fowler up to the outbreak of World War I. He joined up and served overseas with distinction, before going to the English Electric Company in 1919. He rose through that company to become Manager and Engineer of the Traction Department before Hartley persuaded him back to the railway in 1934. Here he was to be the driving force in the development of diesel traction, for which task William was happy to hand over the responsibility. He was, eventually, to rise to CME when Stanier resigned towards the end of the forthcoming war, to devote his full time to Government business.

After studying the results of trials on the shunters, Fairburn recommended that the diesel-electric powered variant be chosen as a baseline. In 1935 twenty 0-6-0 diesel-electric shunters were ordered, 10 from Armstrong, Whitworth and 10 from Hawthorn, Leslie. The Armstrong, Whitworth variant had a jackshaft drive

350 hp 0-6-0 diesel shunter No. 7080 was built by the LMS at Derby in May 1939.

C.J. Marsden Collection

The 1938 3-car diesel-hydraulic set near Bletchley on early trials.   *R.G. Jarvis*

from a single frame-mounted motor and was the variant chosen for subsequent adoption on the LMS. Its introduction was to be somewhat delayed by the events surrounding the industrial reorganisation then taking place as war approached.

The inital order for the production shunter engines and electrical equipment was given to the English Electric Company in early 1939 and production commenced at Derby at the rate of 10 per year until 1942, when wartime needs rather upset the programme.

As with many of these non-standard developments the detail work passing through the CME's department was delegated to a carefully chosen, competent, staff. For much of the diesel work, the design side was given to a Thomas Hornbuckle who collaborated with Fairburn on matters concerning the traction equipment. Hornbuckle was an eminent and far-sighted engineer on the CME's staff, who, after serving an apprenticeship with Hornsbys of Grantham, had joined the MR in 1901 as an electrical engineer. On the MR he had introduced a range of standard electric motors as the Derby works changed over to electric power. Over the years he had risen to the position of Chief Technical Assistant (Electrical) to the CME in Fowler's days. His responsibilities had continued along these lines as Stanier took control.

It was natural, with the success of the diesel-electric shunters, that further diesel applications were considered worthy of development by Stanier. Hornbuckle took note of the undoubted success in Germany of a high-speed diesel articulated passenger unit, the 'Flying Hamburger' which had stolen the headlines in the railway press. Stanier had actually seen this development during the I.Loco.E. trip to Germany in 1936, and it did not prove too difficult to get him to take note of a proposal for a similar development on the LMS. There was also the successful application of diesel power for passenger traffic on the GWR under Collett. William might well have been influenced by this programme initiated under his old boss, and even though he was a strong proponent of the steam locomotive himself, he realised the march of technology would eventually bring about the demise of steam.

Some wind-tunnel tests to determine the best streamlined shape were ordered on a variety of shapes and were carried out at Derby in 1937. The design that was eventually chosen was, in fact, very similar to that of the 'Flying Hamburger'. One main difference was that the LMS development was for a 3-car unit compared to the German 2-car unit.

The genesis for Hornbuckle's 3-car set can be traced back to a 1933 proposal from Beardmore & Co. for a lightweight 3-car diesel-electric unit. Even the shape of the ends of this was very similar to the final LMS set. The Beardmore proposal had also been driven by German railcar developments.

The main difference in the LMS design was that a diesel-hydraulic power train was employed in place of the more usual diesel-electric or diesel-mechanical. The employment of lightweight stock in this proposal was of particular interest to Stanier as this was one feature of research which caught his imagination at this time. He did, we have seen, take a rôle in the development of LMS carriage stock, his predecessors (Fowler and Lemon) having left such matters in the hands of the Carriage and Wagon Engineer, preferring to keep a watching brief on stock design and having little to say in detail applications.

Funds were allocated and in early 1938 the sole example of this big leap forward in railway technology was built at Derby. Its principal characteristic

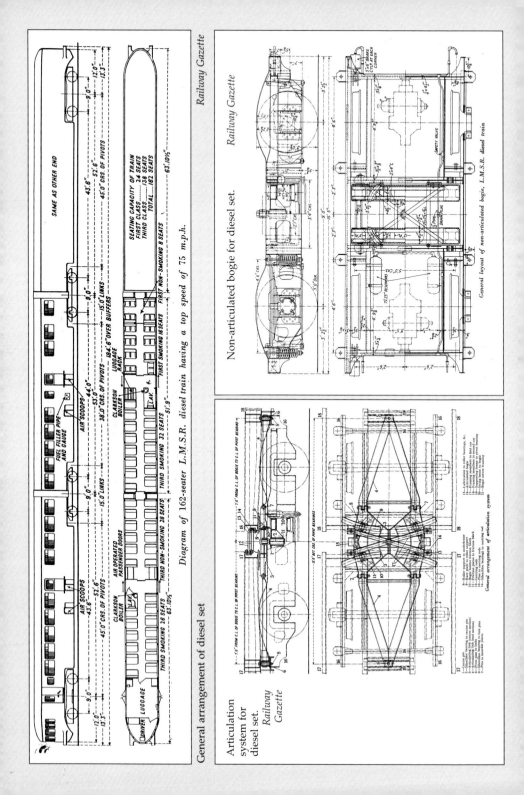

General arrangement of diesel set

Railway Gazette

Diagram of 162-seater L.M.S.R. diesel train having a top speed of 75 m.p.h.

SEATING CAPACITY OF TRAIN
FIRST CLASS . . 24 SEATS
THIRD CLASS . . 138 SEATS
TOTAL . . 162 SEATS

Non-articulated bogie for diesel set.   *Railway Gazette*

General layout of non-articulated bogie, L.M.S.R. diesel train.

Articulation system for diesel set.

Railway Gazette

General arrangement of articulation system

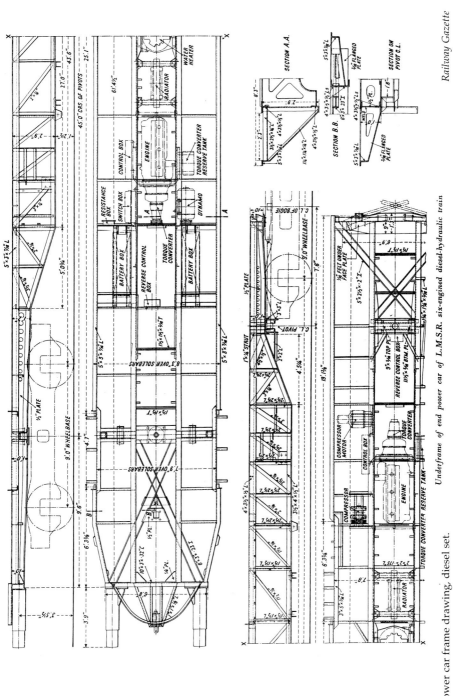

Power car frame drawing, diesel set.

Underframe of end power car of L.M.S.R. six-engined diesel-hydraulic train

Railway Gazette

The diesel set calling at Blunham on the Oxford to Cambridge line, mid-1938.

J.M. Jarvis Collection/MRT

William and Nelle took holidays in Switzerland and it is thought that this photograph is from one of those trips. It may well depict a bit of special treatment by the Swiss Federal Railways.

W.M. Stanier

was that for a total installed power of 750 bhp, no fewer than six engines and transmission sets were installed. Of the eight axles making up the articulated unit, six were driven by the 125 bhp underfloor engines, which were new units developed by Leyland Motors Ltd specifically for railcar work. To cater for individual engine failure a free-wheel facility was built into each transmission set. A maximum speed of 75 mph at the normal maximum engine speed of 2,200 rpm was possible. Traction control was electro-pneumatic.

It was initially put on trial on the Oxford to Cambridge cross-country line. After ironing out any minor snags the set went into regular service on that route, following which it was transferred to the Midland main line for both commuter runs and a high-speed service to Nottingham.

These early trials of the 3-car diesel unit were largely left to the attention of Hornbuckle and one of his assistants, Ron Jarvis. Any modification or rectification was carried out at the Wolverton carriage works where a good job was done at all times. Ron Jarvis oversaw the necessary work and reported back to Stanier that the Works Manager, Merrett, and all his foremen, indeed everyone concerned, had really put themselves out to do what was required in double quick time. Afterwards he suggested that a letter should be written to Merrett, thanking him and his staff for the good work they had done. Stanier's reply was: 'No, I am not going to write them a letter - you can write them one if you like - aren't they paid to do a good job?'

Stanier could never get very enthusiastic about the inevitable arrival of diesel power, he had a deep liking and respect for the steam locomotive and, after attending a paper given by Fairburn on diesels, he is recorded as saying: 'I feel that to devote a whole evening to diesel traction in a country such as Britain is rank heresy.' And at a later paper on rail motors in France he elaborated: 'In England it has to be remembered that the natural fuel, of which there are large supplies, is coal, and the collieries are very large clients of the railway. I suggest that it would be almost a tragedy if we were to introduce the diesel railcar to any great extent though I feel that, as has been the experience in France, there must be certain services where it would be worthwhile introducing a vehicle of this type'.

As the trials of the diesel multiple unit were taking place, a second visit to India for William was called for in connection with a range of Pacific locomotives in use at that time. There were, in fact, three distinct classes of Pacifics employed on the Indian broad gauge railways, the 'XA' lightweight for branch work, and the 'XB' intermediate and the 'XC' heavy main line variants. All were introduced in 1928 and large orders placed thereafter with the classes becoming a standard throughout the country.

In 1937, the East India Railway suffered a catastrophic accident involving one of the 'XB' class Pacifics. On a straight stretch of track near Bihta, when running at some 60 mph, the locomotive derailed and turned over to its left. The leading coaches piled up against the overturned engine and tender, being crushed under the inertia of the rest of the train. 114 were killed in this horrific incident.

The Indian Pacifics had been built in the UK, largely by the Vulcan Foundry and the North British Locomotive Company Ltd. The locomotives had been designed to specifications drawn up the Indian Locomotive Standards Committee which had specified spring controlled leading bogies and Cartazzi

The 1938 Indian Pacific inquiry team, the official photograph.   *W.M. Stanier*

On trials with one of the Pacifics, note the drive for the indicating gear and the base of the shelter on this locomotive. *Left to right:* Mount, Léguille, Carpmael and Stanier.   *W.M. Stanier*

type trailing trucks. For some reason these features resulted in bad riding characteristics on track that was not always maintained to the best standards, resulting in the eventual disaster at Bihta.

With the railways in India under Government control, the authorities immediately sought to set up an inquiry team to find out the cause and recommend the necessary action. Representation to the UK Government resulted in the Chief Inspecting Officer (Railways) of the Ministry of Transport, Col A.H.C. Mount, being requested to form a team to go out to India to assess the situation.

Mount chose his people carefully, with the civil engineering being covered by R. Carpmael the Chief Engineer (Civil) of the GWR. Stanier, who was to cover the locomotive design and operation aspects, received assistance from M. Robert Léguille, the Regional CME (Est) of the French National Railways. Léguille was an accomplished designer who spoke fluent English and German. To present the Indian arguments Rai Bahadur P.L. Dharwan, formerly Chief Engineer (Civil) of the North Western Railway in India, joined the party on arrival in Bombay, bringing with him K.C. Bakhle, a Divisional Engineer of the Great India Peninsular Railway who acted as secretary to the committee. Stanier, as he had done the previous year, was to cover the engineering design, workshop and shed phases of the inspections.

The committee arrived in Bombay on 2nd September to commence their six-week tour. On arrival the special train to transport them was waiting and they began sifting through the data concerning the Pacific locomotives in question.

There were 113 of the 'XA' class in service, plus 99 'XBs' and 72 'XCs', a total of 284 serving throughout the country. Prior to the Bihta disaster there had been 10 derailments of the 'XA' and 'XB' classes, most being put down to severe distortion of the track. However, there were also many reports of all Pacific classes being prone to 'hunting' at speed. Some of the design features of these British-built engines were, it turned out, not really suitable for Indian conditions. The bogie control springs, limiting the sideways movement, were unsatisfactory for several reasons. Firstly the springs were not stiff enough and secondly, Stanier found in his shed inspections that, in many cases, the springs themselves were broken and, more worryingly, that incorrect springs (weaker) had been installed on reassembly of the bogie after maintenance. Also the Cartazzi slides of the trailing truck gave insufficient control on rough track once the locomotive was subject to hunting. On well maintained track the above features would probably have been all right, but the Indian track maintenance was found to be deficient in many ways. Packing of ballast under the sleepers was prone to be washed away during the heavy rains of the monsoon season and severe track distortion resulted. Once these basic facts had been established, Stanier's mind went back to his earlier days on the GWR when different coach bogies were being tested for riding qualities using the 'whitewash' coach, which was arranged to discharge whitewash onto the track every time a lurch was felt. A similar set-up was arranged in a test train and a series of runs made over a particularly bad stretch of track, during which the sleepers were progressively repacked between runs. The evidence was there for all to see - a convincing demonstration of the need to maintain the track to a better standard.

Meantime, the Indian authorities had placed a speed limit of 45 mph on all the Pacifics, to be removed only after modifications recommended by the Pacific Committee had been carried out and approved.

William was to spend much time riding on the three Pacific classes involved, and doubtless this took his mind back to his days at Swindon. He rarely was to be found on the footplate back home; except for an initial ride on a new design he preferred to spend an hour or two cross-examining an experienced inspector in order to gauge the handling and riding aspects of a new locomotive.

Much evidence was also gathered by Stanier on his visits to the workshops and sheds of the seven main Indian railways. He also arranged for a Hallade recorder to be fitted in one vehicle of their special train for a wide-ranging record of track conditions throughout the country.

The tour terminated on the 14th October, by which time they had travelled 7,000 miles, plus 3,100 miles on the footplates of the Pacifics, visiting many of the major cities on the Indian subcontinent. They sailed home from Bombay on the 15th October, arriving back in London two weeks later. A further seven meetings to discuss their findings and complete the report took place in London. The secretary, K.C. Bakhle, had returned with them to enable him to complete the documentation for submission to the appropriate authorities.

A particularly sad message reached William just after sailing home from India. This was to tell him of the death of Sir Henry Fowler, who had been in ill-health for some time in his retirement from the railway scene. He had a considerable respect for that great organiser who had tried, and failed, to overturn the in-built small engine policy on the LMS inherited from the MR at Derby. Stanier, by his judicious handling and cross-posting of the L&YR, LNWR and MR factions in the design offices, had, after a couple of years, achieved a complete turn-about from that disastrous policy.

Much of the recommendations, involving redesign of the bogie springing and Cartazzi slide modifications, plus attention to keeping the track in better order, proposed in the Pacific Committee's report were incorporated over the following months, only to be curtailed by the onset of World War II. The Indian railways had also hoped to carry on their improvements in other areas to be able to plan for 3,000 ton trains, a 12 ft loading gauge, 28 ton axle loads, rails weighing 115 lb. per yard, much larger locomotives, automatic couplings and 100 ft turntables. This ambitious programme never materialised due to the war.

William had more to do in India, but on a totally different and more wide-ranging matter, as we shall see later.

There is evidence from ARLE minutes, although unconfirmed from other sources, that whilst Stanier was in India, he appointed S.J. Symes as Acting CME. If this is so, Fairburn had obviously not yet been short-listed as a possible successor, even though he was becoming quite heavily involved in much of the development work emanating from the CME's department.

Upon his return from India, Stanier took up his Chairman's duties for the ARLE. He attended this body more out of duty than as a need - he did not think much of it as a technical body. However, in 1935 he had become the first LMS CME to be elected to the Presidency of the ARLE. Hughes and Fowler never got that far, although the latter had acted as Secretary for nearly 20 years. He preferred the direct individual approach and once referred to a quite senior colleague as 'rather pernickety, as we say in Wiltshire'. In view of his attitude towards the ARLE, comments attributed to him are few and far between in the minutes of that organisation.

Whilst away in India, the team at Euston and Derby had been busy on some project work on further applications of turbine power. Following the initial success of No. 6202, the 'Turbomotive', Stanier had ordered Chambers to look into the possibilities of a high pressure turbine electric locomotive. Around this time the Union Pacific Railroad in the USA was developing its turbo-electric 'Steamotive', and it was this plus the promising results of the 'Turbomotive' trials which motivated Stanier to suggest this small project study.

In February 1937, Chambers and Cox were dispatched to Paris to inspect a new water-tube boiler, known as the 'Velox', then being fitted to a PLM 4-6-0 on an experimental basis. This was because a water-tube boiler was being considered for the LMS turbo-electric study.

The eventual choice of boiler to be projected was, however, the Lamont type. This consisted of a watertube plus drum, with forced circulation, which was most suitable for the use of coal as a fuel. The resulting design of locomotive was a two-unit affair, consisting of the boiler, fuel and water on one unit with the turbo-generator and condensor on the other. The luckless fireman was to ply his trade in the centre of the first unit and would have endured stifling conditions, rather similar to those found on the Bulleid 'Leader' of later years. The driver had diesel-type cabs at either end of this lengthy locomotive, which it was estimated, would weigh 184 tons. The power available from the traction motors was some 3,000 hp.

However, this project never got further than the drawing board, as priorities changed with the approach of war. The Union Pacific oil-fired design did get built, but it was too late to stave off the inevitable eclipse of the steam locomotive by the recently introduced diesel-electric locomotives in the USA.

So far as Stanier was concerned, his own Pacifics were capable of sustained power outputs matching that estimated for the turbo-electric. A quantum leap such as was implied could not be justified in terms of the return on investment necessary to implement it. The project thus died.

By now, rumours of war were getting stronger and much increasing effort was being put into preparing the railway scene for a return to wartime production needs. Stanier made sure he surveyed the munitions capabilities at all the LMS Works and, in early 1939, had released H.G. Ivatt to head tank design work at Derby.

The Union Pacific turbo-electric locomotive.   *I.Mech.E.*

A family group, Bill, Nelle and Joan.　　*W.M. Stanier*

Chapter Twelve

The Second World War Years - I

As the inevitability of yet another major conflict approached, the LMS, in concert with the other railways, began to plan for that eventuality. In early 1939 wartime headquarters were planned to be sited at The Grove, Watford, away from any onslaught on London. The CME general staff were transferred to Derby and matters were set for the reconstitution of the Railway Executive Committee to consolidate the railway transport infrastructure which would be of crucial importance in the years to come.

In the context of the CME staff move to Derby, there is a story surrounding a political move concerning Hornbuckle, who had shown himself to be a leading light for new developments. He was told it was assumed he would not want to move home, implying that he was not to be transferred. It is not clear who exactly orchestrated this, but all evidence points towards Fairburn, by then Principal Assistant to Stanier. Perhaps Fairburn wished to have Hornbuckle removed from the scene as a potential competitor for CME when Stanier retired - he was 63 in 1939. The reaction from Hornbuckle was to leave the LMS and obtain a high-level appointment in the North East of England.

Stanier, meantime, was preparing for another American trip, this time to present a paper 'Lightweight Passenger Rolling Stock' at the New York summer meeting of the I.Mech.E. This paper had been prepared with Purves and described the latest developments in lightweight stock being introduced on selected trains, particularly the 3-car diesel and the new electric sets for the Liverpool-Southport line. A visit to the USA would also be propitious to back up the presence of the 'Coronation Scot' locomotive and train which had been exhibited earlier that year at the New York Trade Fair, following a very successful tour of the eastern and central states over nine different railroads. The 'Coronation Scot' had gone over with Riddles in charge, having been seconded from his Mechanical and Electrical Engineer's post in Scotland. The team to back him up included driver Fred Bishop, passed fireman John Carswell and a couple of mechanics for routine servicing. The tour was not without its incidents, for after three days the brick arch in the firebox began to collapse and was replaced (two spares had been shipped over with the train) in the Pennsylvania RR works at Harrisburg. This proved to have been installed badly and the second spare was fitted at St Louis by a local boilermaker, Riddles and the chief mechanic. The boiler at that time still recorded 50 psi pressure, so it was a hot job! Also, for the first part of the tour Carswell acted as the driver, for Bishop had fallen victim to pneumonia and was in hospital. No spare crew members being available, Riddles donned a boiler suit and fired the engine. Some of the American railroad staff and Press were genuinely intrigued at the sight of a top executive from the LMS buckling down to some hard manual labour. Driver Bishop rejoined the train at Rochester on 9th April.

Lord Stamp was keen to capitalise on the success of that visit and the tour of the country. He urged Stanier to make this trip even though William was doubtful as to its validity with the clouds of war rolling closer, the former saying that these clouds would 'blow over in a few weeks.'

Lord Stamp bids driver F.C. Bishop and fireman J. McKinnon Carswell farewell at Euston as the train to visit the USA departs from London. It would be some three years before the locomotive returned to the UK. *R.S. Carpenter Collection*

'8F' 2-8-0 No. 8413, a Swindon product of 1943 soon got grimy in wartime use. Seen at Goring troughs later that year! *R.S. Carpenter Collection*

The Staniers (Nelle having accompanied William this time) duly embarked for New York, but by the time they arrived, hostilities had broken out, and they immediately returned on the same vessel under the hazardous conditions of war.

Fairburn had been left as Acting CME whilst Stanier was away on this abortive trip, and on 4th September telephoned R.C. Bond to come to a hasty meeting over breakfast at the Euston Hotel the following morning. At this meeting Bond was told to go immediately to Glasgow as Mechanical and Electrical Engineer, Scotland to replace Robin Riddles, who was being seconded to the Ministry of Supply as Director of Transportation Equipment (a sort of CME by another name in that Ministry).

At the outbreak of war, Riddles, who had returned from the USA earlier, was immediately seconded into Government service. The position was to encompass many other engineering spheres other than the railway one. One in particular was his involvement in the experimental bridging establishment at Christchurch from which came the well-known Bailey Bridge, the Everall Railway Bridge, plus much development work leading to the Mulberry Harbour piers and pierheads. On the railway matters, Riddles is credited with the design and development of the 2-8-0 and 2-10-0 Austerity freight locomotives and the 0-6-0ST general purpose shunting type.

In August 1943, with the LMS in dire need of top management, so many having been drained off for secondment elsewhere, Riddles returned as Chief Stores Superintendent, holding that position until May 1946 when he was appointed as a Vice-President. He was to be involved as the Railway Executive member responsible for mechanical and electrical engineering in the design of several BR standard locomotives, before retiring in 1953.

Having safely landed back in the UK, William was soon back in office, only to be struck down by a rare bout of sickness. This prevented him attending the I.Loco.E. annual dinner as President. Gresley deputised for him, saying 'I am here in the position of a stop-gap. I am very sorry that there has been an engine failure and Stanier has run hot.' Oddly enough, at the next dinner in 1940 Bulleid wired 'Temperature down heart 100% with you', but Stanier deputised for him and opened by saying 'You can appreciate that, the notice being so short, you are not going to get a speech from me - for which you may be thankful.' He added 'I think that the only duty that remains to me, in the absence of Mr Bulleid, is to ask you to drink his very good health and to wish him a speedy restoration to full health and activity.'

The early days of the war were pleasantly relieved by son Bill's engagement and subsequent marriage to Eve Lissenden of Bromsborough, Cheshire. Bill had, by now, answered the call to arms and was commissioned in the Royal Engineers.

As the war progressed, an increasing demand for motive power, plus a cut-back in new locomotive construction, conspired to make Stanier reprieve many old examples which were listed for scrapping. Even a number which had been withdrawn before hostilities commenced, but had yet to reach the cutter's torch, were put back into the shops for a major overhaul to fit them for a few years of war service.

For the first year or so of the war, Stanier's main work was the alteration and equipping of a proportion the works for producing munitions. This resulted in his full-time secondment to the Ministry of Production in 1942 as one of their three Scientific Advisors, his colleagues being Sir Thomas Merton, an old friend, and Sir Ian Heilbron. Stanier's great contribution was that he nearly always knew where and how anything could best be made; for if he did not know himself he quickly found

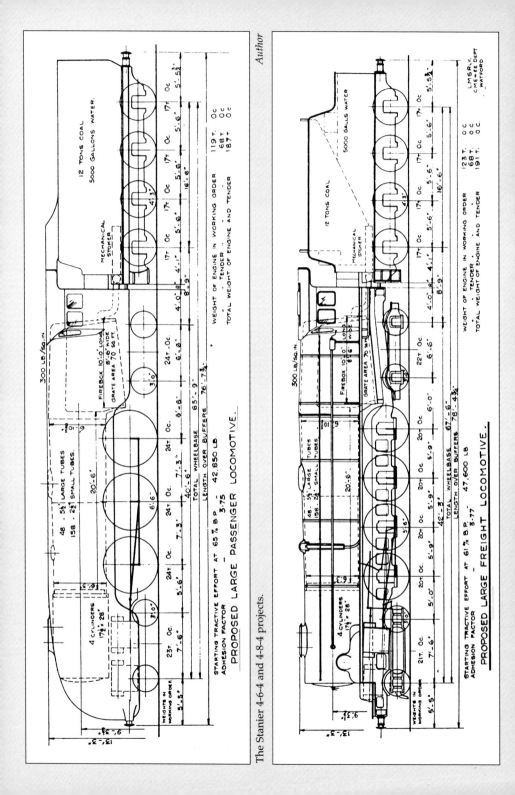

The Stanier 4-6-4 and 4-8-4 projects.

Author

out from his wide circle of friends. The wartime responsibilities began in 1942 when Stanier was given the Chairmanship of the Mechanical and Electrical Sub-Committee of the Railway Executive Committee, which was running the whole of the UK railway system for the duration. In the same year he was asked to fulfil the task of Chairman of the Mechanical Engineering Advisory Committee of the Central Technical and Scientific Register of the Ministry of Labour and National Service.

Meanwhile in 1941 he had been elected President of the I.Mech.E. It so happened that they were in need of a prominent engineer to replace their Secretary, whose retirement was already overdue. Stanier knew that H.L. Guy was retiring early from Metropolitan Vickers and would be an ideal choice. Accordingly, he approached Guy, accompanied by Sir Leonard Pearce to make it more formal, and persuaded him to resign as a Vice-President of the Institution and become its Secretary.

Stanier's Presidential Address in October put over his locomotive design philosophy with a clarity that owed quite a bit, as he readily admitted, to behind-the-scenes work by E.S. Cox. In fact Stanier positively disliked writing and could never get very interested in doing so, which may explain omissions that he later deplored. For example, his 1939 paper failed to credit earlier lightweight carriage work by Agnew of the London Passenger Transport Board, and his Presidential Address overlooked the paper to the Mechanicals in 1906 by Churchward, when he clearly aired his famous design fixes. However, there were, in later years, the odd occasion where he did put pen to paper. One of these has been discovered and constitutes Appendix Four of this book in view of its obvious historical content and appraisal of Churchward amongst other matters covered.

In April 1941, Sir Nigel Gresley died quite suddenly and Edward Thompson was accorded the post of CME of the LNER. Thompson had long been a critic of Gresley's conjugated valve gear fitted to all his 3-cylinder designs. Despite this criticism, from his own staff and elsewhere, Sir Nigel had steadfastly refused to consider any reversion to three sets of valve gear, fiercely guarding what he reckoned to be his personal trade-mark. Thompson immediately took advantage of his new position to obtain an independent assessment of this gear and asked Stanier, whose 3-cylinder designs had all employed three sets of valve gear, to carry out an independent appraisal. On 8th June, 1942 the report was issued. Thompson found all he needed to stop any further employment of conjugated gear on new locomotives. He had, for some reason, an almost pathological dislike of anything Gresley was famous for, and was determined to avoid it in his own designs. The importance of that report cannot be underrated and therefore the complete document will be found as Appendix Three. Although signed by Stanier, the author of the report was, in fact, E.S. Cox.

As William's wartime responsibilities really began to build up, he was delighted to learn of the arrival of a grandson, William Michael, born to Eve and Bill on 14th April, 1942.

Although wartime work took priority, Stanier still found time to get his design team at Watford to scheme at least two types of locomotive to supplement the fleet at the return of peace. The particular schemes of note were, a streamlined 4-6-4 for express work and, a 4-8-4 for fast fitted freight work. Both would have been used primarily on the Anglo-Scottish services. These designs incorporated mechanical stokers as the coal throughput required for

The Royal Society
Burlington House
London

17 March 1944

Sir,

   We have the honour of acquainting you that you were on Thursday last elected a fellow of the Royal Society, in consequence of which the Statute requires your attendance for admission on or before the fourth Meeting from the day of your election, or within such further time as shall be granted by the Society or Council, upon cause shewed to either of them, otherwise your election will be void.

   You will therefore be pleased to attend at half past four of the clock in the afternoon on one of the following days, viz.:

     Thursday   18 May 1944
     Thursday   15 June 1944
     Thursday   13 July 1944
     Thursday

     We are,

       Sir,

     Your obedient Servants,

Alfred C. Egerton
E. J. Salisbury
for A. V. Hill

       Secretaries.

Sir William Arthur Stanier

The notification of election to the Royal Society.   *W.M. Stanier*

their 70 sq. ft grates would be beyond the strength of a fireman for anything but a short time. Their respective tractive efforts, with the 300 psi boiler proposed, would have been 56,070 lb. for the 4-6-4 and 66,330 lb. for the 4-8-4.

These advanced designs were destined to remain as project studies only, as by the time peace appeared the railways were destined for Nationalisation and the motive power needs became more centralised. Stanier also had faded from the railway scene.

The 'Coronation' and its special train had been marooned in the USA at the outbreak of war and it was decided to retrieve the locomotive, when sea crossings were safer in 1942, the carriages being left behind. It was thought the risk worthwhile to bring back the locomotive which could be put to good use on heavy troop and passenger trains. The stock was of limited use and would take up too much valuable space on a ship bringing sorely needed supplies to the UK. The American authorities were told to make the best use they could of the carriages and they ended up as a mobile Army headquarters in Indiana.

During the years 1943-45 Stanier began to mellow, from powerful executive towards influentual adviser. Typically, in a discussion about keeping ashes and water out of axleboxes, he said 'The problem still has to be solved, and I am happy to think that the time has come when I am going to watch how other people do it.' He had, in 1944, resigned from the LMS. A mellowing influence was the showering of honours. Perhaps the greatest honour came in the New Year's Honours List for 1943, in the granting of a Knighthood for services to the railways and the country. The congratulations flooded in from many sources. Very quick off the mark on 1st January were Alan Quartermaine, the Chief Civil Engineer on the GWR, Lord Wigram and Edward Thompson, CME of the LNER who wrote: 'I personally am so concious of all the help you have given me since I took over, thank you so much'. Sir Eustace Missenden, the Southern Railway General Manager, sent his warmest congratulations the following day. The letters continued to arrive for some time; Loughnan Pendred, former editor of *The Engineer*: '10,001 Congratulations! I knew it was coming but was none the less delighted when I saw it in print. No honour could have given greater pleasure to engineers and none could be better merited'.

Proposed by Loughnan Pendred he was elected to the Athenaeum under Rule II as a distinguished person. Proposed by Sir Harry Ricardo he was elected to the Royal Society. Suggested by H.L. Guy, who read the citation, he was elected an Honorary Member of the I.Mech.E. and at a conference in Ottawa he was handed his certificate of Honorary Membership of the American Society of Mechanical Engineers.

In the same year as the Knighthood, Sir William became a member of the Aeronautical Research Council, where his production and mechanical engineering expertise was called for as the railway works increased their output as sub-contractors to the aircraft industry and Ministry of War. And so, as the country began to turn the tide of war, Sir William's responsibilities in his new vocations grew. But he was most certainly capable of the load and much more was to come his way, as we shall see in the next Chapter.

The 1940 Dinner of the I.Loco.E. took place on the 28th February that year. This cartoon depicts those who were present.

H.A.V. Bulleid

Chapter Thirteen

The Second World War Years - II

Not that all the war years were spent at home in the UK, for in 1944, with the invasion forces establishing themselves in Normandy and beginning to push forward into France, the UK Machine Tool Mission was getting ready to journey to India. The party making up this mission consisted of Sir William Stanier as Chairman with R.G. Jarvis representing the railway aspect; Mr S.V. Woolley from the Ministry of Supply; Mr B.W. Palmer, Manager of the Railway Department, Messrs G.D. Peters; and Mr W.H.G. Clifton of the Ministry of Aircraft Production. The Government of India was represented by a former CME of the East India Railway, G.A.R. Trimming who was, at that time, Machine Tool Controller, India.

The task of the Mission was to take stock of India's resources of engineering plant and machine tools, with particular reference to the repair and maintenance of: aircraft and aircraft ordnance; ordnance, including carriages, mountings and ammunition; naval and civilian ships; motor transport vehicles and locomotives and rolling stock.

Having accomplished the above they were to advise on the best use of the resources found in order that India could be made the first base for the operations of the South East Asia Command.

Also they were to advise on the adjustments on distribution and utilization of machine tools as might be desirable.

Their journeyings in India by road, rail and air, after travelling out by sea via the Mediterranean and the Suez Canal, started from Calcutta where, having disembarked, Stanier sent his bearer down to the bazaar to buy him a leather briefcase, with instructions to 'get my initials put on it too'. At that time he had not long been knighted and when the bearer returned with the briefcase it was lettered 'S.I.R.'! He was much amused and apparently not in the least annoyed. 'All right', he said, 'South India Railway, that suits me fine'.

For the rail portions of the travels they travelled mainly in a Great Indian Peninsular Railway touring carriage, half as a sleeping car with four two-berth cabins, and the other half a dining and lounge car with a self-contained kitchen. They covered about 9,000 miles, mainly in this carriage, during the three to four months they were in India, but in the larger cities they stayed in hotels. In the train, in the evenings at about 6.00 pm Stanier would say, 'Well gentlemen, the sun has gone over the yardarm' and he would press the bell. He would then say to the summoned bearer: 'Bearer, chota peg' and they would all be served with a whisky and soda. This duly consigned 'down the hatch' he would say: 'Bearer, the other half'. After this had been consumed, that was the limit of his drinking.

The report that resulted from this Mission was published in November 1944. The general findings emphasised that aircraft spares production was hampered by the lack of skilled labour and such items could best be supplied from plants in the UK and USA. Aircraft power plants, however, were efficiently maintained and repaired, but again spares needed should come from UK and USA sources. Ordnance work was of mixed quality with many of the factories not being fully utilised. There were some examples of efficiently run organisations, notably in the

The Machine Tool Mission at Calcutta, the official photograph. *Left to right in front:* Clifton, Palmer, Trimming, Stanier, Woolley, Jarvis.   *Mrs S. Boorne*

Another group photograph of the Machine Tool Mission, taken on the visit to the Batala Engineering Co.   *Mrs S. Boorne*

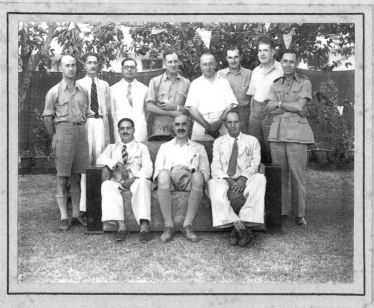

MEMBERS OF U. K. MACHINE TOOL MISSION
AND OTHER OFFICERS AT

The BATALA ENGINEERING CO. LTD., BATALA
(2ND OCTOBER, 1944)

more modern plants. The shipping industry was suffering from a lack of up-to-date equipment and modern shops and, like other areas, a shortage of skilled workers. The maintenance of motor transport vehicles by the civilian plants was poor and suffered from chaotic organisation. Only the IEME and REME depots plus the General Motors plant at Howrah were operating efficiently, the latter particularly well-equipped, and all using line methods of repair and construction.

The locomotive and rolling stock plants, working to maintain locomotives and stock of the Indian railways under War conditions impressed the Mission. Clearly some of the 1938 Pacific Committee's recommendations had been heeded, as the average locomotive availability was running at 85 per cent. However, evidence of crowded erection shops was leading to a longer than desirable major repair time in works of 30 days. The railway members of the Mission thought that with a bit of planning this could be reduced to 21 days. One factor affecting all locomotive work was the lack of a boiler plant in India. Spare boilers were in very short supply, necessitating repairs which in normal times would be considered uneconomic.

R.G. Jarvis was employed to take notes of all the meetings and visits to works, and prepare a report on each day's business which often took him into the small hours, particularly when staying at hotels. On the works visits, 122 in all, Sir William (as Jarvis quoted) 'set a cracking pace with his big driving wheels and I often had to run to keep up with him!'

Ron Jarvis' notes describe some of the little incidents which took place during this tour, the following passage is typical:

> I remember causing him and my other colleagues some worry when I went missing just before we were to leave Bombay. I found that the baboos were making a hopeless mess of getting the baggage to the station and, realising that unless someone did something about it, we should not have it on the train with us. I took charge and got it all to the station, but only rejoined the party shortly before train time, for which I was taken to task. After I had explained the situation, Sir William said, 'I think we owe Jarvis an apology and a vote of thanks'. This is the only occasion I ever recall receiving one from him and he did not even thank his colleagues at the end of the Mission.

Jarvis also mentioned Stanier's loyalty to his staff. Just before they left for India, Fairburn, who had been CME for a few months now, made some remarks to some juniors which were very critical of Stanier. This, commented Jarvis, 'was extremely bad form and rather disgusted me'. Stanier was aware of criticism and disloyalty from that quarter. However, at one place on the tour he was addressed as CME of the LMSR, and he replied: 'I am no longer CME as I have resigned from that position. I have been succeeded by Mr Fairburn, who is a fine engineer.' Here is a measure of the man, brushing off antagonistic behaviour and giving credit to a successor who may not have merited it.

Sir William was a hard taskmaster on venues such as the Indian trip. As he had always demanded at home, any report of a day's business was required first thing the following morning, representing a great amount of paperwork for his assistant.

The Mission concluded on 19th October and sailed home to the UK now basking in the certainty of a defeat in Europe for the Nazi oppressors, for the invasion forces had broken through the German lines and were pressing on towards Germany and victory.

The Stanier treatment to the 'Patriot' did not happen until 1946 under Ivatt. Here No. 45531 is at Derby in 1948 having just received a repaint in a garish green livery with white and orange lining.   *J.M. Jarvis*

The rebuild of the 'Royal Scot' class commenced in 1943. No. 46118 received the Stanier treatment in 1946 and is seen here at Rugby prepared for Royal Train duties, 13th May, 1950.

J.M. Jarvis

The war years were to see some 780 Stanier designs built for the LMS and other railways. By far the greatest number were the 595 class '8F' 2-8-0s turned out, not only by the LMS, but by three private builders as well as the LNER, GWR and SR. many of these were to see service overseas in Turkey, Iran, Iraq, Egypt and Italy.

In addition some 109 'Black Fives' were ordered as well as 58 2-6-4Ts and 18 'Duchess' Pacifics. Additionally, the rebuilding programme planned for the 'Royal Scots' commenced with some 29 dealt with up to 1945.

Sir William had faded out of the picture towards the end of this programme, being fully immersed in his wartime responsibilities. Fairburn had, since the onset of war, had much responsibility in overseeing the necessary work ensuring a smooth handover when Stanier resigned.

In September 1945, Sir William embarked on the SS *Scythia* for a visit to Canada. He was a member of the British delegation to the Joint Conference of Canadian, American and British representatives on Unification of Engineering Standards, held in Ottawa. The ship docked at Quebec on the 18th September, where he was met and conducted to the station by Messrs A.P. Bibeault of the Canadian National Railway and T.D. Slattery representing the Associated British Railways in Canada.

The 1945 visit to Canada. Sir William is about to board the train to Ottawa at Quebec, where he was met by Messrs A.P. Bibeault (CNR) and T.D. Slattery of the Associated British Railways.   *W.M. Stanier*

Bill Stanier in RE uniform.   *W.M. Stanier*

As the war came to a close in 1945, Fairburn died quite unexpectedly, he was only 58. H.G. Ivatt was ordered to take over as Acting CME whilst the Board of the LMS deliberated. They wisely asked Sir William's opinion on the selection and he had no hesitation in recommending Ivatt for the job.

Ivatt was a great believer in using advances in technology to improve the railways, so it was natural for him to consider seriously the potential of diesel-electric power. It was available in an instant, much cleaner than steam and applications elsewhere in the world had proved its efficiency as a means of motive power. Ironically, there had been several applications originating in the UK from private industry but largely ignored by the British railways. However, some export orders had been obtained and limited production commenced by firms such as Beardmore and Armstrong, Whitworth. The revival of interest in the UK was to be on the LMS and Ivatt gladly took advantage of the opportunity to start scheming a prototype diesel-electric, liaising with English Electric. Matters moved so well that the first example of an order for two from that company was delivered just before Nationalisation and began some trial runs. Sir William was present at St Pancras to view the locomotive and watch its departure on a train to Manchester on 15th January, 1948.

The two prototypes, Nos. 10000 and 10001, had 1,600 hp diesels. One locomotive was roughly equivalent to a 'Black Five' and the two, when coupled in multiple, equated to a 'Duchess' class Pacific. In this way Ivatt hoped to be able to compare the economics of steam versus diesel traction in main line service. However, by this time the railways had been nationalised and further development was curtailed by the new management structure planning the future of the new, ponderous, organisation. Sir William viewed all this as an outsider with several consultative and industrial appointments keeping him fully employed. How all this came about is chronicled in the final chapter.

Diesel-electric locomotives Nos. 10000 and 10001 are seen departing Glasgow Central.
R..S. Carpenter Collection

Chapter Fourteen

The Final Years

In the autumn of 1945, a British Goodwill Trade Mission was sent to Egypt and the Middle East to report on the needs of the industrial infrastructure there as it recovered from heavy wartime use. Sir William was a leading member of this Mission. One of many varied items viewed were several examples of the '8F' 2-8-0s awaiting attention after much traffic over the past three years. Maintenance had been minimal, their overall condition was decidedly grubby, yet many were to go on in service for many more years after attention to their needs. The robust construction ensured that their useful lives could be extended for some time yet. In fact, some of the class supplied to Turkey were to last into the mid-1980s on minor duties, one of which has been returned to the UK for restoration and preservation (*see Appendix Two*).

Now entirely divorced from the railway scene, Sir William, at 69, was still full of go, enough for the Ministry to keep him on as a Scientific Advisor for some time after the war. Through their offices he became a Director of Power Jets (R&D) Ltd, then busily employed in developing and improving the gas turbine of Frank Whittle. Also, with his considerable expertise in machine tools, he became a Director of H.W. Kearns of Altrincham.

In 1946 he was still hard at it overseas for the Ministry, this time touring Germany to assess the state of the railway engineering industry after the attentions of the Allied Air Forces. It was while he was going through the Ruhr that Jean Stanier, one of his nieces, who was working in Wuppertal for the Medical Research Council, was invited to accompany him on one of his daily tours of inspection. Jean wrote home on 16th September to describe this unique day for her:

I have had a most exciting day. At 12 o'clock I was collected by two R.E.s (Royal Engineers) who rushed me about 45 miles to a place called Opladen near Cologne. There we met Uncle Will and his special train. He had been inspecting a workshop there. Although the train was passing through Wuppertal later, the Army had decided that it would be better for me to get on the train at 12.50 at Opladen rather than at 1.20 at Wuppertal, so that Uncle Will and I would have longer together, and I would be in time for lunch! We had a very high-class lunch with cocktails and lots of courses, and very high-class company. Uncle Will was such a V.V.I.P. that he wasn't in uniform. After lunch we retired to the super luxury observation saloon at the end of the train, panelled in pear and sycamore. Uncle Will told me about his and Auntie Nelle's Swiss holiday, and Bill (Stanier junior) and Eve's new house, etc. Also the low-down on Power Jets, etc. The military types put in a respectful word here and there. Then we arrived at Schwerte, where we inspected a locomotive repair shop. Or rather, Uncle Will did, rushing on in front and asking lots of questions, while everybody else panted behind. He's obviously expert at that sort of thing; when they showed him huge complicated plans of the workshops he took them in at a glance, and said, 'Why don't you assemble the wiffle-bars in the same place as the wangle-cranks?,' or something equally brilliant. Then we went back to our train (which was guarded by armed police and alsatians!), and had tea in a leisurely manner. At about 5 o'clock we got to Vorhalle where I was met by the

'Newburn', the house in Rickmansworth, is viewed in a water-colour painting here. The
extensive grounds are evident.   *W.M. Stanier*

efficient R.E.s and driven back. Altogether a most efficient and enjoyable trip, and it was
quite pleasant bathing in Uncle Will's reflected glory for a while. He is only in Germany
for a week, and has a very heavy programme. Tomorrow he sees the Krupps works at
Essen and the next day he goes to Berlin. It was certainly very kind of him to entertain
me so nicely, and though I had to work till 11 o'clock tonight it was definitely worth it.

All this travelling still further widened the Stanier sphere of influence and
there were cases of senior appointments being filled 'sight unseen' on his
recommendation. One such was Norman Johnson who had met Sir William on
his 1944 Indian trip and who was in South Africa seeking a new job when Sir
William wrote, virtually offering him the post of Chief Engineer to the British
Pullman Car Co. When Johnson asked if he should return by air to clinch the
job, Stanier, knowing it was already in the bag, cabled back a calm 'No need to
travel by air.'

With the Ministry obligations now very much reduced, Sir William became a
grandfather for the second, and final, time with the arrival of a daughter for Bill
and Eve.

As the LMS recovered after the war, some consideration was given to selecting
standard designs to be chosen for development despite the increasingly clear
indication of forthcoming Nationalisation. The locomotives selected for adoption
as standard types were, the 'Duchess' 4-6-2, the rebuilt 'Scot' 4-6-0, the 'Black Five'
4-6-0, the '8F' 2-8-0 and the 2-cylinder 2-6-4T. All these were Stanier designs and
it says a lot for his engineering expertise that considering his relatively short 10-
year reign as CME no fewer than five of his products were selected for further

On the 19th October, 1950, the Rugby locomotive test plant opened officially. Appropriately, one of the locomotives put on display for that event was Pacific No. 46256 *Sir William A. Stanier FRS.*

J.M. Jarvis

The final accolade from the LMS came when, on the 17th December, 1947, Sir William was asked to attend the naming ceremony of the last but one of his Pacifics, No. 6256. Sir Robert Burrows (son of the GWR chief draughtsman 1905-23, G.H. Burrows) gave the address to which Stanier is replying. *W.M. Stanier*

production in the future. Sadly this programme was halted by Nationalisation, but many of the BR standard designs to emerge instead were derived by Ivatt and Riddles, both of whom had been nurtured under Stanier. The latter had seen that they were positioned for the responsible posts to come their way as he himself faded from the railway scene.

A final accolade from the LMS came in 1947 in the form of the penultimate Pacific, No. 6256, which was outshopped from Crewe with the nameplate *Sir William A. Stanier F.R.S.* Ivatt had left the design largely alone, only fitting a double blastpipe and chimney and roller bearings to update the locomotive.

Undoubtedly, the LMS Pacifics had represented a major technical success for Sir William. Their reliability, once the superheating had been rectified, and their power, placed them into the top class of any express locomotives in the UK. Churchward's principles had been used, with subtle improvements, to produce an outstanding machine. When asked about his design philosophy Stanier said: 'Churchward brought us up to keep everything as simple as possible - no gadgets - the more gadgets you had on an engine meant there was more to maintain.' This comment typifies all Stanier designs. Churchward's common-sense approach at the start of the 20th century had paid dividends.

A lack of hobbies sometimes catches up with old engineers, but Sir William's hobbies remained his family and engineering. His workshop was strictly utilitarian. He was not a gardener, seeing a garden as somewhere to sit in, look at, and distribute produce from. The family enjoyed this. He was always ready for a visit, typically in the Oxford degree days of his nieces and, of course,

Sir William on the footplate of the Courtauld's new Sentinel locomotive, named after him.

W.M. Stanier

Ivatt kept the 'Black Five' in production and in 1947 construction of a batch of 10 incorporating Caprotti valve gear was commenced. Here No. 4748, the first of that batch, is found at Derby shed on 20th March, 1948.

J.M. Jarvis

outings for his grandchildren, Bill's son and daughter. He gave them friendly encouragement in the 'if at first you don't succeed . . .' style and expected them to be tidy and punctual. They were also more amused than their elders by his habit of starting meals last, finishing first, and then turning his chair sideways to look out of the window and drumming his fingernails on the underside of the table. This contrasted with his exceptional patience at lengthy and at times boring formal dinners.

In 1947 Courtaulds had a large expansion programme and they invited Sir William, an active 71, to join the Board part time to direct their engineering policy. He greatly helped their new engineering Director, G. Verrall, and his human touch ironed out most of those fearful arguments between chemists and engineers. When a locomotive was bought for the Grimsby works, Verrall asked Sir William to christen it and unveil the new nameplate, which he had not yet seen. It was *William*. He was highly delighted. Was it a record, an ex-CME with two engines named after him? He remained on the Courtaulds Board until 1958 and as an advisor until 1962.

One of Sir William's many engagements as he approached his eighth decade was the invitation to deliver the 7th Mitchell Memorial Lecture to the Stoke-on-Trent Association of Engineers. This town was the birthplace of Mitchell, who achieved fame as the designer of the Spitfire fighter. Mitchell had actually trained as a locomotive engineer in a local works, and Sir William's former involvement in the Aeronautical Research Council (ARC) made this lecture invitation particularly relevant.

The lecture, entitled 'Locomotive Development - Past and Present' was given on 15th October, 1952 at the Victoria Hall, Hanley. Following Sir William's lengthy presentation, the President of the Association awarded him the Reginald Mitchell Memorial Gold Medal in recognition of his locomotive work and association with the ARC in years past. To some, this invitation to commemorate the memory of a famous aircraft designer may have seemed a bit out of context, but Sir William had been involved with Power Jets for some time and was taking a healthy interest in the application of gas turbine technology for some locomotive applications.

Several drafts of Sir William's lecture still exist and show that he spent a lot of time and effort making it as wide-ranging as possible. Notably, considerable emphasis was given in the opening pages to the pioneering work of Churchward and the influence this had on his followers and locomotive design up to the present day. The Mitchell lecture text which has been uncovered is as close an autobiographical account of Sir William's career as has emerged from his comparitively rare writings. His personal experiences during the Dean/Churchward era and his keen interest in all forms of locomotive development and testing come through as being important factors in his career. It also amplifies the foresight of William Dean in formulating the standardisation programme which was taken up so effectively by Churchward, Collett and Stanier himself. It is the final, amended text that constitutes Appendix Four.

In 1955 came yet another request for a lecture. This time it was the Newcomen Society for the Study of Engineering and Technology. Sir William chose to cover

Sir William and Robert Riddles.

W.M. Stanier

As a past-President of the I.Mech.E. Sir William was entitled to a portrait in the main hall. Here he watches the unveiling.

W.M. Stanier

the life and times of Churchward as his subject. The lecture was given at the Science Museum on 12th October, 1955. It gave a particularly good insight into Churchward's methodical approach to locomotive design and his skills in picking the best young men for the research needed to carry out his ideas in practice.

Add to all this his term as President of the Production Engineering Research Association, 1951-56, and the busy post-railway, post-war Stanier career is seen in full swing.

It was still in full swing in May 1956 when the Council of the I.Mech.E. sent him a telegram 'Congratulations on becoming eight-coupled,' and arranged a birthday lunch. In his brief thank-you speech Sir William recounted the story about an American chemist who was explaining to an engineer all about a new universal wonder solvent that would dissolve anything you cared to name. So the engineer asked, 'What sort of a bucket do you fetch it in?'

The Royal Commission on Awards to Inventors was another body on which Sir William served in post-war years. His wide-ranging engineering expertise was most useful to this Commission, which spent 10 years discussing and reporting to the Government of the day on matters arising from the many schemes put through for its consideration. In May 1956 this body was wound up and Lord Cohen, the Chairman, sent a short note of thanks, together with a copy of the Prime Minister's (Anthony Eden) letter thanking him and the Commission members for their efforts.

There were shadows in 1956 - his wife's health was declining and for some years now several old friends had been passing on. One such loss was the death of C.B. Collett in 1952; Sir William was one of the few attendees at the small funeral for the penultimate CME of the GWR, who had lived a life of splendid isolation since retirement in 1941. Also present was Sir Felix Pole, now sadly completely blind yet determined not to let this affliction prevent his attendance. Stanier also wrote the Royal Society's obituary for Sir Henry Guy, of 'Turbomotive'-fame, meticulously covering his many achievements but kindly omitting the famous Guy characteristic of never suffering fools or obstructors quietly but airing his views about them in a very forthright manner. Sir William Stanier had fully mellowed, and it showed to his colleagues at work and at his reception of the Gold Medal of the Institution of Locomotive Engineers. Sadly, 1957 brought a grievous blow in the death of his wife Nelle, but he was lucky to have an efficient and kindly daughter in Joan to look after him and his house 'Newburn' at Rickmansworth. Upon the demolition of Churchward's old house in Swindon, Sir William had taken the name for his own home, a fitting memory to a greatly admired engineer.

Acclaim kept coming his way - Vice-President of the Stephenson Locomotive Society in 1958 and Guest of Honour at the Crewe dinner in 1959. Col Cantlie was chairman and in his speech credited Sir William with being the first locomotive engineer to become a F.R.S. Stanier promptly interjected, 'No - Robert Stephenson.'

The monthly trip to Kearns at Altrincham for the Board meeting and works visit was a relished duty. Sir William normally stayed overnight at the Crewe Arms and returned from Stockport, alighting at Watford where, as Joan once

Ivatt, Riddles and Sir William at the opening of the Apprentice Training School, Crewe works.

J.M. Jarvis

Joan Stanier - who cared devotedly for her father following the death of her mother.

W.M. Stanier

The Machine Tool Trades Association Dinner, 1958. Sir William shares an anecdote with, *left*, Sir Lionel Kearns and *centre*, Sir Greville S. Maginness. *W.M. Stanier*

Now well into his eighties, Sir William is found at the BR Dinner for Chief Mechanical and Electrical Engineers of all Regions (present and retired) held at the Great Northern Hotel, Kings Cross, 20th December, 1960. *W.M. Stanier*

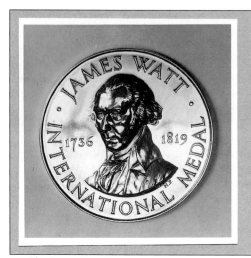 

The James Watt International Medal.   *W.M. Stanier*

Sir William Stanier receiving the James Watt Medal from the President of the I.Mech.E., Mr J.H. Pitchford, MA.   *I.Mech.E.*

confided, she enjoyed seeing his 'almost schoolboy grin' when he spotted her on the station. Travelling with his fellow director, Vice-Admiral Sir Frank Mason, he smoked and chatted enthusiastically, the latter causing the former to steam badly and requiring considerable tamping by his thumb - less elegant than Churchward's specially made hardwood plug. During the electrification of the old LNWR main line they travelled via Derby where Bill Stanier usually arranged to meet the train for a brief chat with his father. Often the subject of conversation would revolve around grandson Michael's progress at Sir William's old school, Wycliffe College, which he had attended since 1950.

Not until 1961, after he was 85, did Sir William suffer slowing-down after a slight stroke; but he went with Joan to South Africa to get over it and in March 1962 the Council of the I.Mech.E. noted that he was 'resuming his duties'. The following year they awarded him the James Watt International Medal. He had been a member for 61 years. Many visitors descended on his home, O.S. Nock and H.A.V. Bulleid amongst them, to seek advice and reminiscences for publications, amongst many things. They always got an excellent reception and meal and he was not at all put off by the occasional appearance of a tape-recorder. He always had a pertinent answer for any mild banter and was always quick to laugh at his own errors, as when he accepted with great pleasure from Riddles the locomotive nameplates 'SIR WILLIAM A STANIER F.R.S.' and decided to mount one in his study only to find it was too long to fit.

He still spent holidays at Sidmouth each year, often visiting the Bulleids who lived nearby. He always claimed he had been lucky to lead a busy life doing things he liked. He often told his family he had been fortunate to live through the golden age of railways. Things had gone well for him, and he had had excellent chiefs and subordinates, he would remark. It was this generous outlook that made him such a universally popular figure so missed when he died in September 1965, aged 89.

The funeral was followed by a memorial service at St Margaret's, Westminster. His old school, Wycliffe, was represented by the Chairman and two other school Council members together with the then Headmaster, for up to his death he had been a faithful attender as President of the Council. The address at this service was given by Sir Frank Mason, who included this apt passage:

> William Stanier is an outstanding example of someone who remained young at heart all his days, and one of his secrets was that he always had time for the younger man. He was able, therefore, to guide and influence younger people. I know, because I am one.
>
> With this youthfulness went a flexibility of mind which enabled him to keep up to date professionally. His approach to everything was simple and direct as befits a great engineer, and he combined this with understanding and kindliness and courage. A wonderful recipe for greatness.

Though many were saddened by his death, here was a man, they were consoled to feel, who would be remembered with pleasurable affection by everyone. A man who had carried the great traditions of Churchward from the GWR to the LMS and speedily and efficiently equipped that line with a range of locomotives to see it through to the end of steam in the UK.

Appendix One

Summary of Stanier Locomotives built between 1933 and 1951

	Class	Type	First Batch	Sub-batches	Total	Notes
'Princess Royal'	7P	4-6-2	1933	1935	12	
	5F	2-6-0	1933	1934	40	
'Jubilee'	5XP	4-6-0	1934	1935-6	191	
'Black Five'	5	4-6-0	1934	1935-51	842	
	4P	2-6-4T	1934		37	
'Turbomotive'	7P	4-6-2	1935		1	
	8F	2-8-0	1935	1936-46	852	
	4P	2-6-4T	1935	1936-43	206	
	3P	2-6-2T	1935	1937-8	139	
Rebuilt *Fury*	6P	4-6-0	1935		1	a
	7P	4-6-2	1937	1938-48	38	b
	6P	4-6-0	1942		2	
	6P	4-6-0	1943	1944-53	70	c
	6P	4-6-0	1946		18	d
	4	2-6-4T	1945	1946-51	277	
				Total	2,726	

Notes:
a High-pressure prototype (Fowler).
b 24 of this class initially built to streamlined format.
c Rebuilds of Fowler 'Royal Scot'.
d Rebuilds of Fowler 'Patriot'.

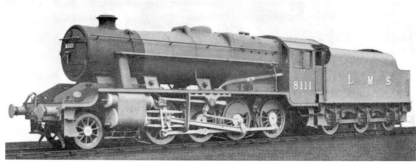

Stanier's '8F'. Here No. 8111 of the 1939 Crewe batch poses in works grey for the camera.
I.Mech.E.

Appendix Two

Preserved Stanier Locomotives

Class	Type	No.	Built Year	Plant	Now found at	Notes
4P	2-6-4T	42500	1934	Derby	Bressingham Museum	
5F	2-6-0	42968	1934	Crewe	Severn Valley Rly	
'Black Five'	4-6-0	44767	1947	Crewe	North York Moors Rly	a
'Black Five'	4-6-0	44806	1944	Derby	Llangollen Rly	
'Black Five'	4-6-0	44871	1945	Crewe	Bo'ness	
'Black Five'	4-6-0	44901	1945	Crewe	Butetown Hist Rly Soc.	
'Black Five'	4-6-0	44932	1945	Horwich	Midland Rly Centre	
'Black Five'	4-6-0	45000	1935	Crewe	NRM Collection	
'Black Five'	4-6-0	45025	1934	Vulcan Foundry	Strathspey Rly	
'Black Five'	4-6-0	45110	1935	Vulcan Foundry	Severn Valley Rly	
'Black Five'	4-6-0	45163	1935	Armstrong, Whitworth	Colne Valley Rly	
'Black Five'	4-6-0	45212	1935	Armstrong, Whitworth	Worth Valley Rly	
'Black Five'	4-6-0	45293	1936	Armstrong, Whitworth	North Woolwich	
'Black Five'	4-6-0	45305	1937	Armstrong, Whitworth	Hull	
'Black Five'	4-6-0	45231	1937	Armstrong, Whitworth	Nene Valley Rly	
'Black Five'	4-6-0	45337	1937	Armstrong, Whitworth	East Lancs Rly	
'Black Five'	4-6-0	45379	1937	Armstrong, Whitworth	Avon Valley Rly	
'Black Five'	4-6-0	45407	1938	Armstrong, Whitworth	Crewe Heritage Trust	
'Black Five'	4-6-0	45428	1938	Armstrong, Whitworth	North York Moors Rly	
'Black Five'	4-6-0	45491	1943	Derby	Midland Rly Centre	
'Jubilee' 5XP	4-6-0	45593	1934	North British	Great Central Rly	
'Jubilee' 5XP	4-6-0	45596	1935	North British	Ingrow	
'Jubilee' 5XP	4-6-0	45690	1936	Crewe	Severn Valley Rly	
'Jubilee' 5XP	4-6-0	45699	1936	Crewe	Severn Valley Rly	
'Royal Scot' 6P	4-6-0	46100	1950	Crewe	Bressingham Museum	b
'Royal Scot' 6P	4-6-0	46115	1947	Crewe	Birmingham Rly Mus.	b
'Princess Royal' 7P	4-6-2	46201	1933	Crewe	Crewe	
'Princess Royal' 7P	4-6-2	46203	1935	Crewe	Midland Rly Centre	
'Princess Coronation' 7P	4-6-2	46229	1938	Crewe	NRM Collection	
'Princess Coronation' 7P	4-6-2	46233	1938	Crewe	Bressingham Museum	
'Princess Coronation' 7P	4-6-2	46235	1939	Crewe	Birmingham Museum	
8F	2-8-0	48151	1942	Crewe	Steamtown	
8F	2-8-0	48173	1943	Crewe	Avon Valley Rly	
8F	2-8-0	8274	1942	North British	Hamworthy	c
8F	2-8-0	48305	1943	Crewe	Great Central Rly	
8F	2-8-0	48431	1944	Swindon	Worth Valley Rly	
8F	2-8-0	48518	1944	Doncaster	Butetown	
8F	2-8-0	48624	1943	Ashford	Peak Rail	
8F	2-8-0	48773	1941	North British	Severn Valley Rly	

Notes

a Experimental locomotive fitted with Stephenson link motion.

b Converted 'Royal Scot' (dates refer to rebuilding).

c Ex WD locomotive, returned from Turkey for rebuilding.

Of the 39 Stanier locomotives in preservation, no fewer than 18 of them are 'Black Fives', certainly a popular design.

Appendix Three

Report on '2 to 1' Valve Gear
LNER 3-Cylinder Locomotives

Chief Mechanical Engineer's Office,
L.M.S. Headquarters,
WATFORD.
8th June, 1942

REMIT:

There are 652 3-cylinder locomotives on the L.N.E.R. on which the inside valve is driven by an arrangement of rocking levers known as the 'Gresley' valve gear. Mechanical trouble has been experienced with these engines, and I have been asked to give a considered opinion on the merits or demerits of this gear and its influence on the mechanical trouble in question.

THE VALVE GEAR:

I have carefully examined the design of the gear from information placed at my disposal by the L.N.E.R. and have supplemented this by an independent investigation into the valve events under various conditions. I find there is an inherent defect which will prevent such a gear from giving correct steam distribution in the inside cylinder under any circumstances, and that this is supplemented by two defects in application which further aggravate the defective distribution.

In theory the movement of the outside valves, as directly driven by normal Walschaert gear, is reproduced exactly on the inside valve, suitably phased to allow for the 120 spacing of the cranks, and the correctness of this movement can be proved mathematically.

In practice, on the other hand, the various leverages are such that any play existing at the various pin joints, adds, and in some cases multiplies in its effect on the middle valve, the final result being that unit play at each of the eight pin joints in the gear is multiplied by eleven by the time it reaches the middle valve. Diagrams prepared by the L.N.E.R. to illustrate this fact have been carefully checked and are correct.

When an engine is new out of the Shops, with no more than the normal manufacturing clearances allowed by the L.N.E.R. in pins and links, namely, .004 in. at each joint, the lost motion at the middle valve amounts to .044 in. With the clearances due to wear which are common experience on engines as returned to the Shops for repairs, this lost motion can amount to more than ⅜ in.

The effect of this varies with the cut-off, speed, and friction of the valve in its liner. The nominal cut-off is exceeded in full gear (65%) by only 3%, but in the case of a nominal 20% the usual cut-off for high speed working, the actual inside cylinder cut-off may be increased to 28%.

The steam port opening associated with this longer cut-off varies under different circumstances. At low speeds or if the friction between valve and liner is high, the inside valve only moves a portion of its normal travel, and then pauses while the remaining movement of the outside valve gear is absorbed by the lost motion. In full gear or late cut-offs this effect is not serious, but in the case of an engine working at early cut-off, where due to the accumulation of carbon or other reasons, the valve is stiff in its liner, the port opening at 20% nominal may be only ¹⁄₁₆ in. instead of the designed ¼ in. so that the steam entering the cylinder is severely throttled and the power developed may be up to 30% below that of the outside cylinders.

On the other hand, at high speeds, the valve, by reason if its inertia, overshoots its expected normal travel by the amount of the lost motion, so that the port opening is that corresponding to the increased cut-off of 28%, namely, about 7/16 in. instead of the designed 1/4 in. and the power developed may now be theoretically up to 30% above that of the outside cylinders.

Between these two extremes, according to the various conditions, the power output of the inside cylinder can vary widely from time to time on a given engine. Indicator cards taken by the L.N.E.R. confirm that at late cut-offs the variation in power development in the inside cylinder is not serious, but at the highest speeds and early cut-offs the power output is sometimes as much as 50% above that of the outside cylinders, shewing that in addition to the over-travel of the valve due to lost motion, there is probably still further over-travel die to whip in the long arms of the rocking lever. There is thus a kind of 'supercharge' effect in the centre cylinder, which may have some bearing on the good haulage performance of these engines in fast running.

Mechanically, the design is unsound because the inherent multiplication of the play in the pins promotes the development of still further play by wear, and the gear can be expected to, and does in fact, become 'run down' at much lower mileage than in the case of the normal Walschaert gear originating the motion in which the leverages are such that the play at the various pins is actually reduced several times by the the time it reaches the valve.

Added to the inherent defect described above are the results of two defects in application. First the various pins and the roller bearings where employed are not adequate in size to offer the greatest resistance to wear resulting from the special circumstances of high leverage and small angle of movement. The following comparison is given with the practice on L.M.S. 4-cylinder engines where, of course, the length of rocking lever arms is much less than in the '2 to 1' valve gear:

	L.N.E.R.	L.M.S.
Main rocking lever pivot Pin Dia.	1½ in.	2⅛ in.
Inside Dia. of ball race	1¾ in.	2⅞ in.
Other pin joints	1½ in. plain bearing	1¾ in. plain bearing 1⅞16 in. needle bearing

Secondly, on most of the engines concerned, the drive to the inside valve is taken from the outside valve spindles after they have passed through the steam chests subject to steam temperature. It is possible to compensate for this to some extent in the setting of the valves, but however set, the variation in steam temperature, which may amount to some 260°F or more in a single run, is sufficient in conjunction with the multiplication afforded by the '2 to 1' valve gear, to effect the movement of the inside valve by a further 1/16 in. The result at early cut-offs is to shorten the effective cut-off at the forward stroke of the piston and to increase it at the backward stroke.

In simple terms, therefore, with this particular valve gear the steam distribution to the inside cylinder will inevitably be irregular and wear of its parts will be rapid. Practical support for this contention is found in the fact that although it was at first applied widely to 3-cylinder engines throughout the world, including large numbers in America and Germany, it has been successively abandoned wherever it was applied, and the provision of three separate valve gears is now standard practice in every important application except on the L.N.E.R.

HOT BIG ENDS:

Statistics furnished by the L.N.E.R. shew that last year, on the 652 engines concerned, ten times as many hot bearings occurred on the inside as on the outside big ends. The number of the former appears to be about 6 times as many as were experienced by the L.M.S. in the same year with 591 3-cylinder locomotives. The high speed engines of the 4-6-2 class of the L.N.E. suffered the highest proportion of failures, the 2-6-2 and 2-8-2 types also being high.

I have carried out a very careful investigation into the probable loading of the inside big end on a typical L.N.E.R. 3-cylinder locomotive, allowing for the inertia forces and the increased steam loading arising from the over-travel of the inside valve which is permitted by a badly worn '2 to 1' valve gear, and I have worked out corresponding figures for the inside big end on the L.M.S. 'Royal Scot' which is an engine comparable in nominal piston loading to the L.N.E.R. 'V2' 2-6-2, and which has been very free from hot inside big ends over the 15 years the class has been in service.

I find that the maximum bearing pressure in the two cases, at high speed, and allowing for the effects of severe wear in the valve gear in the case of the L.N.E.R. engine, is if anything, slightly higher in the case of the 'Royal Scot' engine which has actually a narrower bearing than the former engine, and from a scrutiny of the character of the load diagrams throughout a whole revolution, I cannot say that the poor distribution in the L.N.E. inside cylinder is likely to contribute other than in a minor way to the overheating which has been experienced.

Examination of the design of the inside connecting rod big end, which is common to the whole of the engines in question, does, however, shew certain defects. The most serious are lack of stiffness in the big end strap, and the possibility of the marine type bolts stretching in service, both of which features can cause play between the split brass and its housing, which experience shews can distort the two halves of the brass so that they tend to nip the bearing and cause heating. The L.N.E.R. have realised this, and I was shewn alternative designs of inside connecting rod which should obviate this trouble in future.

Even in the new designs there remain, however, certain features, common also to the original design, which experience on the L.M.S. has shewn to be conducive to hot big ends. These are:-

(1) A brass strip, 1½ in. wide, is allowed to bear on the crank pin on the horizontal centre line instead of continuing the white metal all round each half of the bearing. L.M.S. experience has shewn this to be undesirable since if the adjacent white metal is heated sufficiently it can flow over the brass strip, reduce the clearance, and eventually cause a hot big end.

(2) The white metal used contains 5% lead. Investigation by the L.M.S. Research Department has shewn that the matrix of such a metal will contain a constituent which becomes completely molten at around 185 C. If the working temperature of the big end reaches 100 C, as is possible when the loading bears heavily on the brass strip, this fusible constituent which honeycombs the alloy will begin to flow and smear. The L.M.S. uses a white metal in which the lead is limited to 0.2% maximum. In this metal the easily fusible constituent is not formed, and no melting occurs until a temperature of 239 C has been reached. Mechanical tests shew that this alloy has great rigidity and resistance to creep at working temperature than the somewhat similar alloy containing 5% lead. Some years ago the L.M.S. had several big end bearing failures where exfoliation of the white metal occurred at which the alloy in use was similar to the L.N.E. metal.

(3) The felt pads which come between the oil tube outlet and the journal, continue right across to the outside of the bearing, presumably to give some side lubrication. If badly fitted or worn, much of the oil may escape sideways without getting on to the journal. L.M.S. practice is to enclose the felt pads entirely within the brass.

It is appreciated, of course, that the above three features are also present on the L.N.E. outside big ends which do not experience so much trouble, but under the more unfavourable circumstances of the split inside brasses, and based on a good deal of L.M.S. experience it is felt that they may at least be one contributary feature.

CONCLUSIONS AND RECOMMENDATIONS

(1) the '2 to 1' valve gear although theoretically correct is, in practice, incapable of being made into a sound mechanical job, and rapid wear of the pins, and incorrect steam distribution, are the inevitable results of its use. In view of its inherent defects and the discontinuance of its use throughout the world, a good case can be made for not perpetuating it in any future design.

(2) It is certain that with this arrangement of valve gear it will be necessary to give the engines a frequent overhaul in the Shops and even then it is not possible to eliminate the effect of lost motion due to running clearance required in the pin joints and the effect of expansion on the outside valve spindles on the inside valve.

It is a matter of consideration, therefore, as to whether certain of the classes should not be fitted with an independent inside valve gear.

(3) The excessive inside big end trouble experienced is in my opinion, due mainly to the design of the big end. The alternative designs already developed by the L.N.E.R. should alone bring about considerable improvement. The use of higher grade white metal and the elimination of the brass strip across the bearing are also, in my view, worthy of consideration in view of an extensive experience with 3-cylinder engines on the L.M.S.

(sgd) W.A. STANIER.

LNER 3-cylinder classes on display at a Doncaster works open day in 1936. In the foreground 'P2' class 2-8-2 No. 2003 *Lord President* with 'V2' class 2-6-2 No. 4771 *Green Arrow* behind.   *Author's Collection*

Appendix Four

The Mitchell Memorial Lecture
Given on Wednesday 15th October, 1952
by Sir William Stanier
to the Stoke-on-Trent Association of Engineers

Ladies and Gentlemen,

I am very concious of the honour you have done me in inviting me to give the Mitchell lecture this year. Mitchell was an outstanding leader in the most modern forms of transport.

I represent one of the people who have been concerned with developing the motive power for rail transport which has been the principal means of transport for the last hundred years.

In preparing this lecture on locomotives past, present and future it may be of some interest if a pictorial review is shown illustrating the types of locomotives used to haul the main line passenger trains. Sixty years ago the passenger carriages were mainly six wheeled and the weight was about 18 tons each. Locomotives with a large diameter pair of driving wheels were common on all the Main Line Railways.

On the Great Western, the 'Lord of the Isles' class built in 1851, introduced by Sir Daniel Gooch, were still the principal express passenger locomotives. Its driving wheels were 8 ft diameter with a Tractive Effort of 9,640 lb. This engine was exhibited at the 1851 Exhibition, the Edinburgh Exhibition in 1890, the Chicago World Fair 1893 and the Earls Court Exhibition of 1897 and its driving wheels were at the Festival of Britain Exhibition 1951.

These engines were all for the Broad Gauge and many of them were running at the time of the conversion to standard gauge on May 21st and 22nd 1892.

When I started work in 1892 all the express passenger trains to the West of England were worked by these engines and on occasion they attained speeds of 90 mph. The trains of that day were comparitively light and the coaches were oil-lit with no heating beyond foot warmers.

In May 1892 the Great Western Railway converted all the broad gauge lines to standard gauge, but before this much of the main line had two gauges. The northern section to Wolverhampton and Worcester had always been standard gauge.

At the change of gauge the Great Western as well as most of the other main lines in the country still retained engines with a pair of large diameter wheels for their express services. In 1870, Stirling introduced his 4-2-2, T.E. 11,129 lb. with driving wheels 8 ft 1 in. diameter. 1886, the Caledonian Railway produced a 7 ft single driver, T.E. 13,538 lb. 1897, the Midland Railway the 7 ft 9 in single, T.E. 15,200 lb. These locomotives are typical of what was regarded as necessary to work the trains of their period.

On the standard gauge section of the Great Western and on the other main lines there were many examples of single drive locomotives. In 1891 William Dean, the Locomotive Superintendent of the Great Western, built the 'Wigmore Castle' class as a 2-2-2 with 7 ft 8 in. driving wheels (T.E. 19,000 lb.) convertible from broad gauge to narrow gauge. After conversion this engine was derailed in Box Tunnel on the 16th September, 1893 and after that the engine was fitted with a bogie in front instead of the single pair of wheels and further engines of this class were built and for many years worked main line trains, particularly to Wolverhampton and Worcester from Paddington.

Mr Churchward, when he was Assistant to William Dean, was staying at a country house on one occasion and the small boy of the house asked him how big should be the driving wheels of a locomotive. He replied, '20 ft my son'. The small boy said, 'but you could not have them as large as that'. 'No', said the old man, 'but I would if I could'.

In 1894 Dean built a 4-4-0 locomotive (the *Charles Saunders*) with 7 ft diameter driving wheels (T.E. 16,600 lb.) and in 1895 Mackintosh of the Caledonian Railway built a four coupled locomotive with driving wheels 6 ft 6 in. (T.E. 15,000 lb.).

The increasing weight of carriages and the improvement in lighting and brake arrangement all increased the load that had to be hauled and the Locomotive Superintendents of the day changed over to 4-coupled locomotives for the heavier main line trains generally.

In 1895 Dean built the 'Duke of Cornwall' class for the West of England work from Newton Abbot, and they were the forerunners of a large group of standard classes all having the same arrangement of cylinders, valve gear and rods and in the larger sizes with boilers interchangeable. These classes covered:

The Dukes	5 ft 8 in. wheels	Tractive Effort	18,396 lb.
The Bulldogs	5 ft 8 in. wheels		21,060 lb.
The Atbaras	6 ft 8 in. wheels		16,952 lb.
The Cities	6 ft 8 in. wheels		17,790 lb.
The Aberdares	4 ft 7 in. wheels		25,800 lb.

So much for the locomotives of the past, of which those I have mentioned are typical.

In 1902 Churchward was Chief Assistant Locomotive Superintendent with Dean and carried out the design and building of a 4-6-0 engine, No. 100, with outside cylinders 18 in. x 30 in. and 6 ft 8 in. driving wheels (T.E. 21,734 lb.), and this engine was the forerunner of a long series of standard engines on the Great Western Railway in which new techniques were developed and applied.

The locomotives of the present day all stemmed from those built on the Great Western Railway from 1902 onwards.

George Jackson Churchward became the Chief Mechanical Engineer at that date, and he it was who departed from conventional practice, and introduced and was responsible for the long stroke valve gear, taper boilers and top feed, and a series of standard engines which set the pattern in locomotive practice which after twenty years permeated to all the other railways and are typical of modern practice.

The long stroke valve gear ensured a full opening to exhaust as well as a good inlet for steam, making a free running engine which could use to advantage the full boiler pressure in the steam chest.

The taper boiler provided much improved water space at the throat plate and sides of the firebox, which benefit'ted the circulation and also the surface of the water at the hottest part of the boiler was at its maximum width, so that there was a larger area from which the steam could rise, at the same time the front end with its reduced diameter kept the weight at the front end within reasonable limits.

[Here followed the showing of slides of the Midland Compound and the GWR 'Saint' class as a prelude to the next paragraphs.]

In 1905 Churchward persuaded his directors to buy a de Glehn Compound of the type that was putting up such a good performance in France and in 1905 two large engines of the same type were purchased and Churchward built his first 4-cylinder simple engine, the *North Star* in 1906, as an Atlantic 4-4-2 to run opposite to the French engines which were also Atlantic types.

As a result of the trials he developed the 'Star' class adopting the French type of bogie which is now standard on all Great Western engines and also the L.M.S. engines and has been adopted on the new British Railways' engines, also several other details.

The trial showed that the Great Western engine had a greater capacity and that the 4-cylinder 'Star' as a simple engine was more powerful than the French Compound that could be built inside the British loading gauge. The 'Star' was the forerunner of the 'Castle' built in 1923 and the 'King' in 1927.

The slide now showing [a repeat of slide 12, the 2nd Churchward 4-6-0] gives an indication how Churchward's practice permeated the Great Western policy and this is the commencement of present day practice.

In 1906 Churchward read a paper to the Institution of Mechanical Engineers and in the discussion Loughnan Pendred, the Editor of *The Engineer*, suggested that it might be an advantage to discharge water into the steam space. Churchward seized on the idea and developed the top feed which discharged the feed water from the injectors into the steam space near the front end of the boiler, preventing the sudden cooling of an area of tubes which may cause tube leakage and, more important still, acted as a perfect means for liberating any oxygen in the water before it got to the tubes and plates.

These engines formed the basis of the present day locomotives as these practices have extended since 1924 to all the other railways.

In 1910 Churchward arranged an exchange of engines with Mr Bowen Cooke of the L.N.W. Railway and as a result Cooke built the 'Claughton', a good engine, but it missed one of the essential features of the *Polar Star*; that was the valve gear of the 'Claughton' operated the inside valve from the front end of the outside valve on to the front end of the inside valve so that the expansion caused by the temperature of the steam on the outside valve added to the expansion of the inside valve rather upset the valve events and the steam distribution.

Why was Churchward able to proceed with such confidence?

From the days of Gooch the Great Western had been using a dynamometer car which enabled the drawbar pull of the locomotive to be recorded and measured. Churchward developed this device and built a new dynamometer car and these slides give a view of the interior showing the instrument table, also the records that were obtained from the various graphs produced on the paper.

Then in 1904 Churchward was so impressed by the work of Professor Goss of Purdue University, U.S.A., that he obtained authority to build a locomotive testing plant and on this he was able to indicate the steam inlet and outlet of the cylinders of the new engines, find out the vacuum in the smokebox and many other things which were difficult to obtain in actual service, but he always supplemented these tests by trials on the road. As a consequence he developed a technique which became the accepted practice on all the other Railways since 1924.

In 1924, at the Wembley Exhibition, the Great Western exhibited the *Pendennis Castle* (built by C.B.Collett, who had succeeded Churchward) which was an enlarged edition of the 'Star' class built by Churchward. Alongside was a very fine Pacific built by Sir Nigel Gresley of the L.N.E.R. In 1925 Gresley and Collett arranged to exchange engines, and as a result of the trials Gresley was convinced that there was something in the long stroke valve gear and altered his design to incorporate this feature with very advantageous results.

In 1927 Collett built the 'Kings', and Fowler the 'Royal Scots'. The 'King ' class were a further enlargement of the 'Castles', but with 6 ft 6 in. driving wheels (T.E. 40,300 lb.), built especially for the heavy trains to the West of England. One of the highlights of this year was the visit of the engine *King George V* to the U.S.A. to the Fair of the Iron Horse on the Baltimore and Ohio Railroad. The engine created somewhat of a sensation and a common remark was that it looked like an automobile and not like a locomotive.

The 'Royal Scots' on the L.M.S. were a great advance on the engines previously built for the L.M.S. Railway and have been responsible for some excellent work on the very heavy road to the North and to Holyhead.

Experimental Engines

In the meantime a number of experimental engines had been built. In 1905 Mr (afterwards Sir) Cecil Paget who was Works Manager of the Midland Locomotive Works Derby, obtained permission to build an experimental engine. This engine was a radical departure from conventional practice. It was a 2-6-2 engine with eight single acting cylinders 18 in. diameter 12 in. stroke, four connected to the middle axle and two to each of the other coupled wheel axles.

The valves for the cylinders were of the rotary type and although very ingenious they were the weakness of the design as at that stage of metallurgical knowledge it was not found possible to keep them tight without the risk of seizing up with variations of temperature. The boiler was unusual in as much the walls of the firebox were brick and only the crown was integral with the boiler barrel.

Sir Hugh Reid in association with Ramsay built a steam turbine locomotive with an electric drive in 1904. It had two bogies each of 4-4-0 type and was equipped with a locomotive boiler, turbine engine and condenser with an electric generator and motor drive to the four main axles.

In 1920 Sir Hugh Reid and Macleod built a geared steam turbine condensing locomotive. It had two bogies each comprising two driving axles and two carrying axles. The rear bogie was fitted with a high pressure turbine and the front bogie with a low pressure turbine.

In 1921 the Ramsay condensing turbo-electric locomotive was built by Sir William Armstrong Whitworth & Co. The boiler was carried on one vehicle with a 2-6-0 wheel arrangement and the turbo generator and condenser on another vehicle of 0-6-2 wheel arrangement.

Ljungstrom Turbine

One of the most interesting experimental locomotives built in this period was the Ljungstrom turbine locomotive built by Messrs Beyer, Peacock of Manchester in 1926 and which was run for some months on the Midland section of the L.M.S. Railway. It consisted of a ten wheel vehicle carrying the boiler and another vehicle with 6 coupled wheels and a bogie carrying the turbine and drive and condenser. The boiler was pressed to 300 lb./sq. in. and at the smokebox end was a feedwater heater and a turbine driven fan to provide the draught for the boiler. The turbine drove through a train of gears the main drive on one pair of the coupled wheels and this was provided with a quill and flexible connection.

The condenser was air cooled by means of four fans driven with an auxiliary 300 hp turbine. The main turbine developed 2,000 hp at 10,000 revs and the main gear box had a tumbler gear on an eccentric bearing, which could be engaged when the steam valve was closed and the engine was standing to provide a reverse motion.

In 1927 Messrs Kitson of Leeds built a diesel steam 2-6-2 locomotive in which the diesel end of the cylinder was used for continuous work and the steam end for starting, for overload and for auxiliaries. The water cooling for the diesel cylinders was used for boiler feed and the drive was through a geared shaft and jack shaft with connecting rods to the wheels.

| T.E. at start and to | 6 mph | 24,500 lb. |
| T.E. at | 45 mph | 7,000 lb. |

In 1930 the L.M.S. had built by the N.B.Locomotive Co. an engine with a Henschel Schmidt high pressure boiler. It was generally the same as the 'Royal Scot' class but the boiler had a closed circuit 12/1600 lb./sq. in., the high pressure section 900 lb./sq. in., and

The Test Plant at Rugby. Two views of this facility when under construction in 1939.

(Both) I.Mech.E.

the low pressure section 250 lb./sq. in. There were 4 [in fact only 3] cylinders - two HP [one] 11.5 in. by 26 in. and two LP 18 in. by 26 in. giving a tractive effort of 33,200 lb.

Difficulty was experienced with the closed circuit section and after an unfortunate accident the engine was withdrawn and in 1935 rebuilt as a modified 'Scot' (*British Legion*).

In 1930 Sir Nigel Gresley built a 4-6-4 locomotive with a water tube boiler. The boiler was built by Yarrow and with a working pressure of 400 lb./sq.in.. The engine was a compound with two HP cylinders 12 in. by 26 in. and two LP 20 in. by 26 in. After running experimentally it was rebuilt as a 3-cylinder simple with a standard Pacific boiler.

In 1935 the L.M.S. Railway in association with Messrs Metropolitan Vickers built a 4-6-2 locomotive with the boiler of the 'Princess Royal' but with a turbine driving through a three stage gear reduction and a quill to the leading coupled wheels. This engine has run a regular train service until the last year and has run about 250,000 miles. As extensive repairs were required, the last time it was stopped it was decided to rebuild it as a standard 'Princess Royal' engine and it now runs under the cognomen of *Princess Anne*. [In fact, just a week previous to this lecture, the rebuild had been involved in the Harrow disaster involving three trains, and was to be scrapped as being beyond repair.]

In 1932 I joined the L.M.S. Railway as C.M.E. and it was my duty to review the locomotive requirements and to endeavour to standardise the classes of locomotives required for the various duties on the railway.

The more urgent need was to provide a locomotive for the very heavy trains to and from Scotland, and the first Pacific locomotive on the L.M.S. was built at Crewe in 1933. The 'Princess Royal' had a tractive effort of 40,000 lb. [actually 40,300 lb., the Coronation class was 40,000 lb.] with a large boiler capacity.

In 1937 the first 'Coronation' class were built and these engines became the main line express locomotives for the heavy services to Scotland, Manchester and Liverpool.

The first batch were streamlined and tests on models in a wind tunnel confirmed that some advantage was gained at speeds of 70 mph and over. Later engines were built without the streamlined casing and it was difficult to justify the additional cost of the covering.

In the meantime it was realised how important it is to measure the work done and the L.M.S. and the L.N.E. Railways combined in a scheme to provide a locomotive testing station and modern dynamometer cars to work in association with it. A new dynamometer car was built and at the same time the L.M.S. and L.N.E. Railways jointly decided to build an up-to-date locomotive testing plant at Rugby.

The French railways had recently installed a testing plant at Vitre and every facility was given by them to see what they had done and to hear what improvements they themselves thought necessary. The locomotive testing station at Rugby is I think the most up-to-date and complete in the world today.

The recording table was supplied by Messrs Amsler of Switzerland and the opportunity was taken by the L.M.S. to obtain a similar table for the new dynamometer car and also a similar hydraulic head for measuring the drawbar pull. Fortunately these were delivered just before the war started but were put into cold storage until after the war. Now they have been completed and form very important instruments to provide information to assist the design of all new locomotives of the British Railways.

Lomonosoff developed in Russia a very successful technique for locomotive testing by maintaining a constant speed and a good deal of work was done in Poland and on the German State Railways. The general principles originally laid down by Lomonosoff (1913, 1925 and 1926) have formed the basis of all subsequent testing.

In 1936 the L.M.S. Railway considered the possibility of constant speed testing and Mr H.I. Andrews of the L.M.S. Research Department prepared a scheme which was approved and three vehicles were built by the L.M.S. They are electrically controlled with self contained power units and resistance units. The maximum performance specified called for an absorption of 51,500 lb. tractive effort between 10 and 12 mph and of 3,000 continuous horsepower between 22 and 120 mph.

'Black Five' No. 44765 in the yard of the Rugby Loco Testing station, 1st June, 1950. It is all ready to be connected to the test plant, being festooned with the connections and piping for indicating the cylinders and taking various pressure and vacuum measurements.   *J.M. Jarvis*

'Black Five' No. 45218, still with a domeless boiler, at speed on the Rugby Test Plant.
J.M. Jarvis

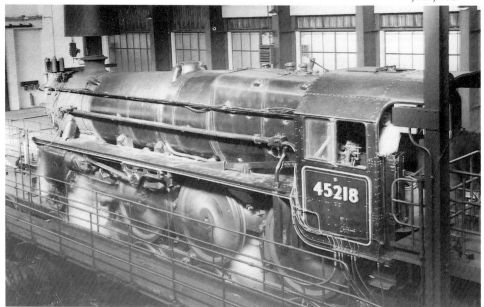

Depending upon the power and speed of the test to be made, it was possible to use 1,2 or 3 mobile units and so control the speed of the train by either assisting or retarding the locomotive to maintain constant speed.

The train, designed for tests at constant speed, consists of Dynamometer Car No. 3, Mobile Test Units Nos. 1, 2 and 3, and a special tender.

Dynamometer Car No. 3 which can also be used separately for normal testing on revenue earning trains, contains four main working compartments: viz.

(1) The leading brake compartment, containing the Electrical Grate-weighing apparatus, Electrical Boiler Water Level Indicator, and a pneumatic tender water-level gauge.

(2) The main instrument room. This accommodates the control desk for the Mobile Test Units, an instrument panel which carries four multipoint thermometers, three draught gauges and a barometer, a power supply panel and the main recording table. This last is driven from a flangeless road wheel hung from the leading bogie. The dynamometer proper is hydraulic, of Amsler make. The chart records, in order, speed, inertia force, buffing, drawbar pull, drawbar horsepower, work done against inertia forces, work done at drawbar, time (seconds), time (minutes), distance and location, water from tender, and twelve pens for other records as required. Relative wind speed and direction can also be recorded if desired. The chart normally moves proportionally to distance but can be run on a time base. The speedometer, horsepower meter, inertia and drawbar work integrators are of Amsler spherical type. A telephone system connects table and control desk with all parts of the train and with the footplate.

(3) The indicator compartment. This contains a Farnborough indicator furnishing indicator cards on a crank-angle base.

(4) The gas-analysis compartment, for continuous smokebox gas sampling and analysis during tests.

Mobile Test Units

These are braking units, which can automatically keep the speed constant irrespective of gradient by varying the load as required. Each has four 375 hp blower cooled generators driven from the axles, current generated by each is dissipated in separate blower cooled resistance banks. No.1 unit with nose suspended generators, has a maximum speed of 50 mph while Nos. 2 and 3 have quill drive and maximum speeds of 90 mph and 120 mph respectively.

Control is applied from the Dynamometer Car and speed can be regulated by hand or automatically. Controls are duplicated on the units to allow of their use without the dynamometer car if required. A diesel generator set in each supplies current for control, excitation and auxiliary purposes.

The units may be used singly, in pairs, or all together according to the speed and braking force required for each individual test.

Special Tender

The coal space is divided centrally, one side being used for test coal in hundredweight bags, the other for similar coal loose for when not running under test and for standby purposes. A steam winch is provided for loading. A water meter is fitted, recording water taken by the injectors on the Dynamometer Chart. A through corridor permits communication between footplate and train. The tender capacity is 6 tons coal and 3,500 gallons water.

It will be seen that the records shown give the mile posts, drawbar pull, the work done, etc. But all these records were affected by the variation in line, whether it was up hill or

One of the three mobile test units referred to in Sir William's lecture.   *I.Mech.E.*

Sir William explains some technical detail with the use of a model of an '8F' 2-8-0 after the
Mitchell Memorial Lecture.   *W.M. Stanier*

down. It is difficult to find a length of line so level that it will give constant road speed tests so that the Mobile Test Units are used to either accelerate or decelerate the train to maintain constant speeds.

What of the future? I am no prophet, but I think there will be an increase in the number of diesel rail cars on feeder lines and for intermediate services. Electrification of some of the busy sections may be justified, particularly for suburban services around large towns.

The possibilities of gas turbines for locomotives are being examined and experiments are being carried out with coal as the fuel either as a producer or as pulverised coal.

Atomic energy is in the distant future but a great deal of research is still required before it can be applied for generating power, even for stationary plants.

Author's note:

The lecture was illustrated by over 50 slides starting with some GWR broad gauge locomotives and early GWR stock, and included pictures of most of the engines and equipment mentioned in this excellent summary of locomotive development over nearly 100 years. The audience certainly got a first class appraisal of how Churchward influenced locomotive design for the rest of steam days on the British railway scene.

Mitchell Lecture Illustrations

1. GWR 'Lord of the Isles'
2. Stirling 8 ft single
3. Caledonian Rly single
4. Dean 2-2-2
5. Dean 4-2-2
6. Dean 4-2-2
7. Dean 4-4-0, *Charles Saunders*
8. Dean 'Duke' class
9. Mackintosh (CR) 4-4-0
10. MR Johnson single
11. Churchward 4-6-0 No. 100
12. G.J. Churchward?
13. Midland Compound
14. GWR 'Saint' 4-6-0
15. de Glehn Compound 4-4-2
16. LNWR 'Precursor' 4-4-0
17. Churchward 'Star' as 4-4-2
18. LNWR 'Claughton' 4-6-0
19. GWR stationary experimental engine
20. GWR Dynamometer car
21. ditto
22. ditto
23. Test data from dynamometer car trials
24. ditto
25. ??
26. *Pendennis Castle* at Wembley (1924)
27. 'King' class 4-6-0
28. *Royal Scot*
29. *Royal Scot* on train
30. Paget 2-6-2 locomotive
31. Reid-Ramsay turbo-electric locomotive (1904)
32. Beyer, Peacock/Ljungstrom turbine locomotive
33. Kitson Diesel-steam 2-6-2
34. *Fury*, 4-6-0
35. *Fury* as rebuilt
36. Gresley 4-6-4 water-tube locomotive
37. Turbomotive, No. 6202
38. No. 6200
39. Streamlined 'Coronation' class 4-6-2
40. above on train
41. ditto
42. ditto
43. BR Standard engine (probably a Pacific)
44. New dynamometer car (LMS)
45. ditto
46. ditto
47. ditto
48. Special test vehicle
49. ditto
50. ditto
51. Gas turbine locomotive
52. ditto
53. ditto
54. ditto

Bibliography

A History of the LMS by O.S. Nock, George Allen and Unwin
British Locomotives of the 20th Century by O.S. Nock, PSL
British Pacific Locomotives by Cecil J. Allen, Ian Allan
Churchward Locomotives by Brian Haresnape and Alec Swain, Ian Allan
Collett and Hawksworth Locomotives by Brian Haresnape, Ian Allan
Crewe Locomotive Works and its Men by Brian Reed, David and Charles
Derby Works and Midland Locomotives by J.B. Radford, Ian Allan
Fowler Locomotives by Brian Haresnape, Ian Allan
Great Western Saints and Sinners by Dr W.A. Tuplin, George Allen and Unwin
History of the Great Western Railway by Peter Semmens, George Allen and Unwin
'Lightweight Passenger Rolling Stock' by W.A. Stanier, Paper for I.Mech.E.
    Summer Meeting in New York, 6th September, 1939
LMS 150 by Patrick Whitehouse & David St John Thomas, David and Charles
Locomotive Adventure by H. Holcroft, Ian Allan
Master Builders of Steam by H.A.V. Bulleid, Ian Allan
Proceedings, Institution of Mechanical Engineers
Sir Henry Fowler - A versatile life by J.E. Chacksfield, Oakwood Press
Stanier Locomotives by Brian Haresnape, Ian Allan
The British Steam Railway Locomotive 1925-1965 by O.S. Nock, Ian Allan
The Great Western Railway by Frank Booker, David and Charles
The Great Western Stars, Castles and Kings by O.S. Nock, David and Charles
The GWR - 150 Glorious Years by Patrick Whitehouse and David St John Thomas
    (editors), David & Charles
The LMS Pacifics by J.W.P. Rowledge, David and Charles
'The position of the Locomotive in Mechanical Engineering', W.A. Stanier
    Presidential Address to the I.Mech.E., 1941
'Triple-Car Diesel Train for the LMSR', *The Railway Gazette*, April 1938
'Under 10 CMEs' by E. Langridge, *SLS Journal*
UK Machine Tool Mission Report, Government of India Press 1944

Sir William at the I.Mech.E. summer meeting 1960, held in Dublin that year. The 'crack' appears good, no doubt lubricated by the local brew.   *W.M. Stanier*

Index

References to illustrations are shown in **Bold**.